HORRIE

the war dog

Also by Roland Perry

Fiction/Faction

Bill the Bastard

Programme for a Puppet

Blood is a Stranger

Faces in the Rain

Non-Fiction

Pacific 360

The Changi Brownlow

The Australian Light Horse

Monash: The Outsider Who Won a War

Last of the Cold War Spies

The Fifth Man

The Programming of the President

The Exile: Wilfred Burchett, Reporter of Conflict

Mel Gibson, Actor, Director, Producer

Lethal Hero

Sailing to the Moon

Elections Sur Ordinateur

Bradman's Invincibles

The Ashes: A Celebration

Miller's Luck: The Life and Loves of Keith Miller, Australia's Greatest All-Rounder

Bradman's Best

Bradman's Best Ashes Teams

The Don

Captain Australia: A History of the Celebrated Captains of Australian Test Cricket

Bold Warnie

Waugh's Way

Shane Warne, Master Spinner

Documentary Films

The Programming of the President

The Raising of a Galleon's Ghost

Strike Swiftly

Ted Kennedy & the Pollsters

The Force

HORRIE

the war dog

The story of Australia's most famous dog

ROLAND PERRY

ALLEN&UNWIN
SYDNEY • MELBOURNE • AUCKLAND • LONDON

First published in 2013

Allen & Unwin
Sydney, Melbourne, Auckland, London

83 Alexander Street
Crows Nest NSW 2065
Australia
Phone: (61 2) 8425 0100
Email: info@allenandunwin.com
Web: www.allenandunwin.com

Cataloguing-in-Publication details are available
from the National Library of Australia
www.trove.nla.gov.au

ISBN 978 1 74331 799 0

Internal design by Midland Typesetters, Australia
Set in 12/16 pt Adobe Caslon by Midland Typesetters, Australia
Printed and bound in Australia by Pegasus Media & Logistics

20 19

MIX
Paper | Supporting responsible forestry
FSC
www.fsc.org
FSC® C008194

The paper in this book is FSC® certified. FSC® promotes environmentally responsible, socially beneficial and economically viable management of the world's forests.

CONTENTS

To Jim Moody's wife Joan, and their children Ian and Leonie
and the memory of Jack Grossman

'The life he had led had etched itself into his face'

1
SACRIFICE

Jim Moody parked his car near Sydney's Quarantine Station, in the inner west suburb of Abbotsford. It was 11 a.m. on Friday, 9 March 1945. The life he had been leading over five years of war service in several theatres north and south of the globe had etched itself into his sun-tanned features. For someone aged 33, he had a drawn if not haggard expression, accentuated by a black moustache. Moody began walking with a little white terrier-cross on a leash. It was hot. He felt like a beer before, under strict government orders, he faced the moment of handing the dog over to the Quarantine Station. He entered a dimly lit pub, featuring dilapidated pictures of footballers and beer advertisements on the walls. Moody sat at the bar under one uncertain roof fan that battled the humidity.

Three stools away was a huge, sweating man wearing a singlet, shorts and sandals. His behind was so big that it seemed to consume the seat. The man turned to scowl at his unwanted 'companion' at this drinking hour reserved for alcoholics. Moody noticed two scars: one on the man-mountain's right shoulder and the other on his right arm. Then he recognised the outsized, twisted pug's nose. At that moment the big man did a double-take, looking down at the dog sitting on the sawdust covered tiles and then at Moody.

'Jesus!' Ray Wallace said. 'You're Jim bloody Moody! You saved my life in Jerusalem!'

They reached across and shook hands.

'Is that Horrie?' Wallace asked with a frown.

'Yep.'

'He looks older.'

'He is a few years older than when you met him in '42.'

Wallace turned to the young barman. 'A beer for this man and a dish of milk for the dog.'

'We don't serve dogs, Ray.'

'You bloodiwell do this one!' Wallace snapped. Pointing down, he added, 'This is Horrie. He's famous!'

The barman put down the glass he was drying and peered over the bar.

'Yeah, I've seen him in the papers!' the barman said. 'Wish I had my camera!'

'Just worry about the beer and milk, mate,' Wallace reminded him before turning to Moody, and adding in admiration, 'I'll never forget that chair you smashed on that bloke's back! His knife was aimed straight at my guts. Then crash! Down he went, flat as a pancake and out like a light! All I got was a cut on the shoulder.'

They chatted for a while about their war experiences. One beer became three. Moody looked at his watch.

'Better be off, mate,' he said.

'One other thing,' Wallace said, his ruddy face brightening like a beetroot. 'I got off with one of the nurses at that Jerusalem hospital you took me to after the fight.'

'Which one?'

'Can't remember her name.'

'Bonnie?'

'Yeah, that's it, Bonnie.'

Moody's heart sank. Bonnie was an attractive redheaded woman who, the night before the chair-smashing incident, had rejected his overtures in a Haifa hotel.

'Jeez she was great!' Wallace chuckled. 'Nursed me beautiful!'

Moody winced a smile and felt a little ill. It wasn't the sort of demoralising news he could cope with at that moment.

'Where you off to, Dig?' Wallace asked.

'Got to see a man about a dog.'

*

Mr John King, the very tall, skeletally thin man at the white-painted, cold front office of the Abbotsford Quarantine Station, was firm but polite in dealing with the handover of the dog.

'What do you plan to do with it?' Moody asked as he bent down to pat the dog.

'That's up to Mr Wardle, the Director of Hygiene,' King said, bending his hunched shoulders forward to glance at a photo of Horrie with Moody in the *Daily Mirror* and then back at the dog.

'I wrote to him but he did not reply,' Moody said.

'Mr Wardle will reply, I assure you. He is a very efficient director.'

Moody was nervous. He filled his pipe and lit it.

'When will I know his . . . er, decision on . . . er . . . Horrie?' he asked.

'You'll have 24 hours notice if he . . . um . . . decides to dispose of the doggie. Otherwise he will be quarantined for several weeks.'

The words chilled Moody.

'Won't make a decision today, will he?'

'Oh, good heavens, no. He plays golf late on Friday afternoon. He won't even consider the case until Monday.'

'Are you open Sunday?'

'Yes, 11 a.m. until 5 p.m.'

'I'll be in to see Horrie then,' Moody said, looking down at the dog. It had a baleful expression. His tail wagged for a second or two but stopped when he saw Moody striding off. Moody went to another pub, smoked his pipe and had more beers alone before driving home to his temporary postwar lodging in St Peters, in south-west Sydney.

*

At about 5 p.m. King reached Wardle in Canberra after several failed phone calls.

'Make it quick,' Wardle said, 'I've got golf!'

'Yes, sir . . . er . . . we have Horrie.'

'Good, good.'

'Mr Moody wanted to know if you were going to reply to his letter.'

'Oh, yes.' Wardle groaned. 'I'll make sure he receives a reply, Monday, no Tuesday, the day after you have put it down.'

'You wish it destroyed?'

'Yes, yes, I most certainly do. Only inform Moody a few minutes before it's done. I don't want him creating a protest noise with the press, or any ratbags such as the World League for the Protection of Animals that may try to hold up proceedings. We always have trouble from those do-gooders.'

'Mr Moody brought with him a vet's report saying the doggie was in very good condition. No sign of any disease.'

'Probably a fake. Moody is a slippery customer. Just think of how he transported that animal in North Africa, Greece, Crete, Palestine and Syria, and then sneaked it into Australia; an animal that could be infected with some Eastern disease. Even his name, Horrie the "Wog" Dog, should tell you something. "Wog"—illnesses . . . This animal may be full of diseases we don't even know about!'

'But I rang the vet—a Mr Kimber of Swan Street, Rosehill—who wrote the report. It's authentic.'

'I really don't care, King,' Wardle said, irritated. 'Must be made an example of. Can't have any soldiers smuggling pets into our country. Rabies kills, as you well know.'

'So, we are to do this for reasons other than the doggie's condition?' King asked but Wardle had already rung off. He was late for his game.

*

Moody turned up on Sunday, 11 March, at Abbotsford to see the dog and found Horrie sleeping in a cage. A bowl of meat sat untouched inside the door of the cage.

'He sleeps a lot,' King said, 'and he is off his food. Is he always like this?'

'Not really,' Moody replied carefully, 'but being separated from me can cause him some anxiety.' He noticed King had a bandaged right hand. 'Did Horrie do that?'

'Yes. He can be vicious. I'm very pleased he doesn't have rabies. You know that we recommend that dogs should be put down if they draw blood?'

'I know that. But you must remember, Mr King, that this is a war dog. He saw quite a bit of action.'

Moody changed the subject and asked: 'Have you heard from Wardle?'

'No,' King lied, 'I still don't know what he wants to do.' Seeing Moody's concern he added, 'If it was up to me, sir, I would not put him down, at least not for the way he entered the country. He is in good condition. You've looked after him well. The only problem now with letting him live is that other servicemen may be encouraged to break the law.'

The dog woke up and took in Moody. His tail wagged.

'I'll try to feed him,' Moody said. King nodded. Moody opened the cage door and beckoned the dog. He rolled off his mat and sauntered over to him, his eyes still sorrowful. Moody patted him and stroked his back. The dog seemed to relax. Moody offered him a piece of the meat.

'What is this?' Moody asked King. 'Kangaroo meat?'

'Yes.'

'He's probably never had it.'

The dog sniffed the piece, looked at Moody as if in two minds over whether to bite him or take the food, and then opted for the food. Moody tried to induce him to eat the rest by himself but the dog would only be handfed, which was a delicate business.

'He certainly trusts you,' King said.

'Yeah, well, we've been on a long journey, haven't we, Horrie?'

When the dog had eaten several portions, Moody again patted and stroked it, then stepped out of the cage. The dog whimpered. Moody felt uncomfortable.

'So when will you let me know?' he asked, struggling with his emotions.

'As I told you on Friday, soon as we know Mr Wardle's decision.'

Moody took one last glance at the dog and left. He would never forget that look of qualified trust, of hope, of despair, of a life poorly treated. Moody wanted a drink to drown his sorrows but had to wait until he was back at St Peters. Over a beer on the back porch, the consoling former sergeant of his platoon, Roy Brooker, told him: 'Got some good news. Your best mate Gillie is back tomorrow. We can have a nice old reunion of at least some of the Signals lads. I'm told just about all the boys will be back in town soon.' This brightened Moody a fraction but he had a restless night worrying about the quarantined dog and its fate.

At 3.55 p.m. on Monday, 12 March, Moody received a call from King: 'I have bad news, Mr Moody. Under Quarantine Regulation Number 50, your doggie is to be put down at 4 p.m.' Moody looked at his watch.

'You've given me five minutes notice!' Moody roared down the phone. 'You said I'd have a day . . . !'

'I am sorry about this, I really am, but it was not my decision. Good day, sir.'

*

Brooker took Moody to the pub, where they sat drinking, smoking and reminiscing for several hours. They drove into Sydney's Chinatown for a meal, and then returned to St Peters at about 9 p.m. Brooker opened the door and ushered him into the lounge, saying, 'Another beer, mate?'

'No, I'm pretty shick—' Moody said as Brooker switched on the light. Moody shook his head in disbelief as members of the close-knit Signals group of the 2nd AIF's 1st Machine Gun Battalion—'the Rebels'—pressed forward cheering and yelling, 'Surprise!'

It was the beginning of an all-night party. To understand why these recent war veterans celebrated the death of an innocent little dog, we must go back four years to a remote North African desert during World War II.

2

DESERT ANGEL

Once Australian Prime Minister Robert Menzies told Australia, in his melancholic and dutiful way, that his country was at war with Germany on 3 September 1939, battalions sprang up everywhere with an anticipation which demonstrated that memories of the Great War 1914–1918 were short. More than 160,000 Australians had been either killed or wounded in that brutal conflict mostly 20,000 kilometres from home. Yet barely a generation later, tens of thousands, including many who had served in World War I, were quick to join up again. Could they have been driven by a belief that brutal dictatorships everywhere had to be stood up to after the invasion of Poland? Well, that was the idealistic propaganda, and many would respond to it. Was it to preserve the British

Empire? That was a bit of it. Was it a sense of boredom for some and a sense of adventure through travel overseas for others? This had to be another motivation. Humdrum lives would galvanise into the disciplines and hardships of armed forces at war. Yet a sense of camaraderie for young men with a grand common cause—to defeat fascism—was an over-arching drive.

One of the first outfits to form up and consolidate at Sydney's Victoria Barracks on 14 December 1939 was the 2nd Australian Imperial Force's 1st Machine Gun Battalion. The battalion, which was part of 6th Division, marched through Sydney streets on 4 January 1940, taking the same route as the 1st AIF soldiers had in 1914. After the training period, the battalion of about 500 members embarked aboard the *Orford* and left for the Middle East in May 1940. But it was diverted to Britain to bolster that country's defences and it reached Gourock in Scotland in mid-June. The 18th Brigade and the Machine Gunners next took a train to England and camped at Salisbury Plain while the Battle of Britain raged in the skies above them. In November 1940, the Battalion sailed on the *Otranto* from Colchester for Egypt in the Middle East. On 29 December 1940, it docked at Kantara on the Suez Canal, a name that evoked memories for some of the men who had been with the victorious Anzac Light Horse under General Harry Chauvel from 1916 to 1918 in the desert war that saw the Turks pushed out of the region after 400 years of rule.

The next day the men disembarked and were pleased to leave the overcrowded ship. It was better even in the dry desert where they were accosted by locals wanting to sell them everything from cheap miniature pyramids to uninviting food and drink. The next day, New Year's Day 1941, the battalion left by a train of cattle and goods wagons for a journey 30 kilometres west of Alexandria, as the crow flies. The men wished they had wings after the wearying 14-hour journey with many tiring stops en route as the wagons were shunted this way and that. They eventually encamped, still on the first day of the year, at Ikingi Maryut on the fringe of Libya's desolate Western Desert. Once at the destination, the fatigued Machine Gunners were to await orders to join the battles against the fascist armies of Italy, and Germany if it entered the region too.

The battalion units began by erecting a series of tents on the barren landscape, which evoked a scene like a travelling circus. But there was little fun to be had. The Western Desert was a dull area, if not forsaken by the gods then definitely by water, for there were no rivers running into it from the Mediterranean. The vast desert region south, west and east of the nonexistent Ikingi city was an ancient underground necropolis with a patchwork of catacombs harbouring decaying remnants of civilisations long disappeared. The only sign of life among the rock and never-ending sea of sand was the occasional camp of the Bedouin, who wandered the desert as they had for thousands of years.

But for the moment, early in 1941, two close mates and despatch riders of the Gunners' Signals Platoon, Jim Moody, 29, and Don Gill, 22, were doing their best to make their experience in the wilderness more lively by combining their love of motorbikes with practice for their fast-approaching role in delivering messages from headquarters to the front and vice versa.

Fit, lean-as-a-drover's-dog Gill gunned his Norton motorcycle through the desert looking for Moody, maintaining a top speed of more than 100 kilometres an hour. Every day, while waiting for their call to the battle zone further east, he and Moody went through a riding routine that they hoped would stand them in good stead for what lay ahead. For, although they would not always be on the front-line with their machine-gun–toting mates, they would be expected to ride into the war zone and deliver vital messages to commanders. Similar to ambulance men and others, they would risk their lives as much as the soldiers perched in trenches behind their weaponry. On open tracks, wadis and oases, through ravines, down and up hills and mountains and into trenches, the despatch riders would attempt to deliver their often vital messages. They would run the gauntlet of planes spitting bullets and dropping bombs, hidden snipers and the pot luck of running into an umbrella of artillery shells, along with the even more hideous stretches of landmines. Somehow on their roaring bikes, pushing them to the limit, and 'hidden' behind goggles, they had an instant sense of invincibility, in a similar way the Australian troopers had on their mighty Walers two decades earlier. Those hardy horsemen trotted, galloped and thundered through the deserts of the same region with a similar increased sense of bravado or courage afforded by their fearless mounts. Now the horses had been overtaken by mechanisation: by speedy motorcycles, cars, trucks, armoured vehicles, tanks and planes. It made the war zone seem far smaller—and more dangerous.

Gill and Moody had both ridden motorbikes in Australia since they were young teenagers. They competed in racing competitions in the decade before the war and were members of 'bikey' clubs, the more innocent forerunners to the later 'gangs.' Moody had developed exhibition tricks and they both loved their jobs now. If they were going to be in the thick of war, they very much appreciated the thought of hitting it, being in it and at times running from it, on bikes in what they regarded as 'sport.'

'Better than sitting in a bloody trench waiting like my uncle did on the Western Front through freezing winters,' Gill said often, 'or stuck in a sea of mud unable to withdraw while artillery rained down on your skull.'

He and Moody loved speed and feeling some wind against their faces, even in the near breezeless desert, as they bounced over rocks, ploughed on sand or zoomed over gullies, unworried by a crash or breakdown, for each despatch rider knew his bike better than his own body. They spent hours each day fixing, rebuilding, polishing and nurturing these most precious two-wheeled vehicles, among their best 'mates' in the desert, nearly as important to them as the lifeblood of the desert itself: water. Motorbikes were the Walers of World War II.

On this day, 19 January 1941, Gill was pushing his machine harder than ever to catch up to Moody in their daily game of acclimatising to the desert. The lead rider would charge ahead on a dead straight course and after a specified time put compass instructions on a piece of yellow lined paper under a pile of six rocks—always six. The follower would have to find the rocks and pursue the course again, dead straight until the next rock pile and so on.

Gill spotted Moody's bike first as he careered over a dip in the desert. Then he saw him standing, pipe in hand, about 80 metres away examining something. At first Gill thought it must have been a rock. The nuggetty Moody, an amateur geologist, had a fascination with any formations, even carrying stone fragments in his kit in the hope of taking them back to Australia. But this time Moody was stock-still, watching. Gill approached. Moody turned and waved as he heard the roar of the oncoming bike.

'What's up, mate?' Gill asked as he stood his bike and removed his goggles.

Moody pointed to a small white animal about twenty metres from him.

'Looks like a . . .' Gill began, 'a pup.'

'Yeah. It's got floppy ears. I'd say it's only a few months old.'

'I saw one like that in Alexandria. Some sort of Gypo terrier. Got bowlegs like a bulldog, but the face says terrier. And that long body looks like some sort of sausage dog. That stub of a tail says he's been doctored.'

The dog was no more than a foot high. It seemed oblivious of the company it had attracted. His mind was on catching geckos. He would lay flat and wait until he noticed movement in the sand. His floppy ears straightened and fell as it picked up sound in the near-soundless terrain. Then he would pounce. But his quarry seemed to be too quick. For a moment the dog had been distracted by a bird of prey circling high above. It would have been looking for snakes, asps or other reptiles. Or perhaps it was waiting for the little dog to tire.

'What's the bloody little beggar doing out here, miles from anywhere?' Gill asked.

'Might have been abandoned by Bedouins.'

'Maybe.'

'Or Italian refugees fleeing west?'

Gill moved close.

'*Eh, bambino*!' he called in a nasally drawl. The dog ignored him and did not look his way. 'Can't be Italian.'

'With your vowel-crunching Aussie accent?' Moody said with a laugh.

They moved close. The pup noticed. It looked up. He was alert. His body language was defensive as he backed away a few paces and then stood his ground. He growled. He bared sharp, strong incisors for such a modestly sized mutt. Experiences with humans may not always have been good.

Moody took a sandwich from his pack and offered it to him. The dog was suspicious. He didn't even sniff it.

'I like his attitude,' Gill said, 'this little fella can't be bought, even if he's starving and by the look of his rib cage, he's not far off.' Gill dropped to his knees, as if he too were searching for lizards. Soon both men were copying the dog in its predatory games. They noticed the anguish in his face as his attacks proved fruitless. He was weak but determined. Yet he persisted trying to lift stones with his nose to find the disappeared geckos, which were several wriggles ahead of him. After a few minutes, he took a breather, looking plaintively at his new companions whom he was still not prepared to trust. There was a frown of frustration in his look. His tongue was out.

Moody took a water bottle from his kit and a small bowl. He put water in it and placed it a few metres from the dog. He looked at it, then back at Gill and then the dish again. He waddled over to the bowl. He sniffed it for several seconds before drinking in such haste that it was obvious he had not had water for some time.

'Flat-out like a lizard-hunter drinking,' Gill commented with a gentle laugh. 'I really like the little bastard.' He looked at Moody. 'Are you thinking what I'm thinking?'

Moody nodded. The drink had won over the dog. He wagged the stub of his tail and licked both men in turn, who sat in the sand with him. The dog rested his tired little head on Moody's arm. This sign of affection, but also pathetic resignation for his plight, touched both men.

'Can't leave him out here,' Gill said, looking up at the hawk-like creature, circling lower. 'That damned buzzard is easy big enough to whisk him away in his claws.' He glanced at Moody. 'What do you reckon?'

'Let's take him back to camp,' Moody smiled.

'Good idea,' Gill said, 'we can work out what to do with it there. At least we can give the little bloke a decent feed and drink.' He looked up at the big bird above. 'And deprive something else of a very decent feed.' They wandered close to their bikes. The little dog waddled after them, his tail wagging. He looked up with a querulous, even hopeful expression.

They decided that it would be dangerous to ride with one hand free and one holding the dog. Instead Moody picked him up. The dog did not object but instead tried to lick Moody's face. Then Moody rode pillion with the dog as Gill started his machine with a roar that had the big bird above winging away higher.

They would come back for Moody's bike later.

3

THE REBELS AND THEIR DOG

Gill and Moody introduced the pup to the members of their tent of Signallers, who called themselves 'The Rebels.' This title was more wishful thinking than fact, although several of them were daring to the point of being foolhardy. They all shared either distaste for any form of authority or a downright hatred of it, and in this sense they were rebellious. Their main overall crime was to be AWL—Absent Without Leave. But their reputation preceded them and had consequences. If the cook-house was raided during the night, police came to the Rebels' tent first to make enquiries. At least one member of the 'gang' seemed to be wearing a black eye after a day's leave, indicating that the individual had been in a brawl. They were an undisciplined bunch, and it was this that bound them.

The engineering genius of this specialist communications group was also the quietest: 30-year-old, brown-eyed George Harlor, who had dark hair and a complexion to match. He was the group's techno-nerd. He could scrounge around for odd bits of metal and wire and put a wireless together in no time. The lean, 176 cm Harlor renamed himself 'Gordie' because he was irritated by all the Arabs calling each of the gunners 'George.'

New South Wales farmer Bert 'Fitz' Fitzsimmons, 24, was the tallest of the group at 182 cm, and the sharp-witted one who had a quick reply or observation in any moment. Fitzsimmons was obsessed with running two-up schools. The 175 cm Lance Corporal Brian Featherstone ('Feathers'), solidly-built and with his hair the colour of straw, was the youngest at 19. A shipping clerk in civilian life in Victoria before the war, he had the look of a callow yet bright youth. His conscientiousness and outstanding ability as a signaller had seen him gain a promotion early. But his tendency to fool around had made his holding on to that one stripe a tenuous thing.

There was also South Australian former barley inspector Bill Shegog, 26. 'The Gogg,' at 178 cm, was a wry-humoured character and the best signaller among them. He was also a good sportsman who, it was claimed, could kick an Australian Rules football over a wheat silo and hit a cricket ball out of sight. When any footy or cricket team was picked, he was always everyone's first choice. He had a real talent for alcohol consumption, and in a culture which lauded 'big drinkers,' he was reputed to be the biggest of the entire battalion to the point where some dared call him 'The *Grog*.' Just to balance things, he was the battalion's champion chess player. Shegog also had a creative bent, and was a fine artist with pencil or paintbrush, and everyone had their portrait done by him. All were astonished at their likeness and Shegog's capacity to capture the subject's 'personality.' When asked by Fitzsimmons if his creativity at chess and painting came from his drinking, he replied: 'Nope. I just happen to be a drunk who paints and plays chess. I'd get out the easel and the chessboard even if I didn't drink.'

'Just like Hemingway and Scott Fitzgerald? They were drunks and creative writers . . .'

'I'd give a qualified "yes" to that. But please don't accuse my paintings of being bleak, humourless landscapes like their books, which I believe is *because* they drink.'

Finally there was sandy-haired, rough-shaven and unkempt Malcolm Gordon Murchison, 22, who was never too far from trouble or danger. The 180 cm former car salesman 'Murchie' was the wildest and most slovenly of an untidy bunch, the exception being the neat and well-pressed Featherstone. Murchison had the habit of idly playing with his revolver and firing a bullet into the roof of the tent. Apart from being unnerving for the others, it let in little rays of hot sun that irritated those trying to avoid the heat of the day. He also kept everyone ill at ease by keeping several 40 to 50 centimetre-long desert snakes—asps—in a kerosene tin under his bed. Every so often he would bring them out and play with them, causing much displeasure with his tent-mates, who would scatter.

The not-so motley crew was under the charge of Sergeant Roy 'Poppa' Brooker, the 47-year-old veteran of the group, who served under General Chauvel with the 9th Light Horse Regiment in the Middle East in World War I. He and Moody were the only two married men. The lean yet sturdily framed, 172 cm Brooker was partially bald. He preferred the comb-over to the brush-back of his dwindling hairline, which was the only sign of insecurity or mild self-absorption in an otherwise natural and generous leader. He would say in defence of his men that the first Anzacs were the wildest men on leave, but 'once on the front-line and in battle, they were the most disciplined and alert of all armies.' This tough former Victorian railway clerk wasn't sure this steadiness under real pressure translated to his lot, but he said he 'lived in hope,' and he was often found defending the indefensible among his Rebels for their range of minor misdemeanours. While Brooker complained they were a 'useless bunch,' he had a hidden pride in them and was respected and loved by each man, who knew that he had their interests at heart. They described him as a *fair dinkum Aussie*, which, coming from them, was the highest praise an NCO, or any enlisted man, could receive. Brooker had endeared himself to the Rebels early in their stay at the Ikingi 'resort' when Moody, the Rebels' amateur geologist and archaeologist, found a battered skull in a cave, which may well have been an ancient grave. He took it and a chunk of marble from the cave back to the tent and suggested the skull would make a fine mascot (before Horrie).

'It has a real grin,' Fitzsimmons observed, and this caused much mirth in the tent as each man agreed it was a smiley, if bony face. They called him 'Erb' and placed the skull above the tent door. The camp's most unpleasant member, bespectacled Queenslander and Sergeant-of-the-Guard Ross 'Gerry' Fitzgerald, a brutish drunk, abused the Rebels for keeping it, saying it was 'bloody sacrilege' to take an 'ancient' from his desert tomb. He tried to take 'Erb' from the top of the tent door. Brooker confronted him.

'I'll fight you for him,' Brooker told Fitzgerald, rolling up his sleeves as if ready for a fisticuff. The 188-centimetre Fitzgerald was the camp tough-guy bully but, for once in a sober state, he was not prepared to take on the fierce-looking Rebels' sergeant.

Fitzgerald backed off, saying: 'I wouldn't want to hurt you, old man, not over a grinning bloody skull!' This caused howls of derision from the onlooking Rebels. From then on, Brooker had greater respect from his men.

*

The day Horrie was found, the Rebels were all lying around in the tent, some happily preoccupied; one or two were reading and writing letters, while the others were fiddling with guns, radio sets or other pieces of equipment to do with signalling. The little canine wandered in and galvanised interest. Moody and Gill explained his plight.

After offering him bully beef, which he ignored, biscuits, which he crunched through, and water, he played up to anyone who garnered his attention with a whistle, a snap of the fingers, a word or even a smile. His stump of a tail gyrated. He was an instant hit. All the Rebels had some 'country' in their backgrounds and they loved animals, especially dogs. They all had an instinct about him. The dog with no name at that moment except 'doggie,' 'mate,' 'little fella,' 'cobber' or 'boy' moved from bunk to bunk as if acquainting himself with every one of them by sight and fragrance. He was sensing them and his position in the scheme of things.

'What's his name?' Harlor asked as he oiled a piece of equipment.

'Didn't tell us,' Moody replied, which elicited smiles from all of the others.

'What are you gunna call him?' Featherstone asked. 'Make a darn good mascot, I reckon.'

''Bout time we had a mascot,' Fitzsimmons said, 'instead of Erb or Murchie's bloody reptiles.'

'They are not "reptiles,"' Murchison said, 'they are my pets.'

'Nar,' Gill said with a rueful look, 'they can hardly lead our unit on a march.'

'So it's agreed then,' Brooker remarked as he hoisted the dog up onto his bunk, 'he's with us and he's our mascot.' He noticed a flea jump from the dog, then another. 'Once he's had a good bath.'

'Why?' Gill asked. 'He'd be cleaner than most of us.'

'Speak for yourself,' Brooker said.

'Okay, fellas,' Moody interjected, 'let's name him.'

Each man proffered a name or two. First, there was 'Anzac' but that was dismissed. One of the other battalions had a cat of that name. Second, there was 'Gypo,' the nickname for Egyptians, which was not always expressed with endearment. That was discarded. Murchison commented that such a name linked him with the locals when this dog might become a 'dinkum Aussie.' A third suggestion was 'Wog Dog,' which brought a ripple of approval. Some repeated the name and liked the rhyme. But once more Murchison thought that this linked him to Arabs in general, and they were not popular with the diggers, who had not come to terms with the locals and their ways, which were so different from those 'back home.' This blatant racism was common among troops of all nationalities but the anti-Arab attitude had roots deeper than simply a sense of superiority, often unjustified, because of different cultures and mores. The troopers of the Australian Light Horse during the Great War had had a deep and abiding distrust of all Arabs, who were lumped together, whether city dwellers or desert nomads. The thieving of items such as rifles and the sly murdering of troopers in the camps throughout the Middle East had set the original Anzacs hard against all Arabs. The massacre of British cavalrymen in the Sinai at Oghratina on 23 April 1916 had begun the detestation. Continued pilfering, throat-cutting and shooting of Anzacs in the night over the next two years had set a level of wariness and hate that lasted for the war's duration. It had carried over two decades into this war, and was reinforced by renewed thieving experienced already by Anzac troops. Nevertheless 'Wog Dog,' which sounded good to the men and had a resonance of fun, in keeping with this funny little animal and his playful, alert ways, looked likely to win the naming 'contest.'

'You can call him that,' Murchison said, 'but I won't.'

'Think of it as standing for Worthy Oriental Gentleman,' Fitzsimmons proffered and drew grins all round. Someone asked for a typical Aussie name and several were suggested. Just one stuck. Every one of them knew a 'Horrie,' and all agreed that anyone so named was a good bloke.

'Okay,' Gill concluded, 'he's Horrie the Wog Dog.'

'Just Horrie for me, thanks,' Murchison interjected.

Each man got the dog's attention by motioning to him and calling 'come 'ere Horrie!' The pup bounded from one bunk to another. And when he was exhausted he plonked himself in the middle of the floor, glancing at each man as he called to him. His sharp-nosed little face was a twitch of interrogation, as were his oversized ears that fell and rose at different angles, and not always in unison, as the cogs of his instinctive brain tried to comprehend what was going on. He didn't mind the cry of 'Horrie,' but he seemed to bristle if it was accompanied by a laugh, especially if the mirth seemed to be aimed at him. When Murchison guffawed at his every reaction, Horrie leapt to his bunk and grabbed a sock. He then bounded to the tent flap as if intent on running off with it, which stopped the tormentor's derision. The dog led the now irritated Murchison on a clumsy dance around the bunks.

'Okay, all right, Horrie, mate,' Murchison said, as if contrite, 'I won't laugh at you again, promise.'

The dog waddled over to him. Keeping his eyes on Murchison, he lowered his jaw to the floor and let the sock slip out.

'My God,' Brooker exclaimed, 'I have never seen a dog behave like that! It's as if he understood every word!'

The others applauded and made approving noises.

'Goodonya, Horrie!' 'Atta boy, Horrie!'

'If he's as game as he is intelligent,' Shegog observed, 'he is going to be a real Anzac.'

As he spoke, Horrie leapt on to Murchison's bunk where he had hauled his kerosene tin from under it. Horrie was agitated. He charged at the tin and barked, knocking off the lid. In a flash, he was snapping at the snakes inside it. The tin clattered to the floor. The biggest of the reptiles, a half-metre long asp named Cleo, slithered out, causing a couple of the men to ease away. Horrie jumped from the bunk and snapped at her. Cleo coiled as if ready to spring, just as three other snakes eased and undulated in several directions. Murchison grabbed at them, taking his mind off the confrontation between Horrie and Cleo. The dog lay flat without taking his eyes off his would-be quarry. Cleo looked ready to thrust her fangs into her four-legged foe. For a moment the room fell silent. The only sound came from Horrie as he emitted a low growl, his ears straight up and unified. He was blocking out all other noise.

'For fuck's sake, Murchie!' Shegog whispered. 'Do something before—'

The asp's head darted at Horrie, her fangs bared. The dog was a fraction quicker as he leapt sideways one way, then the other before grabbing the snake high on the neck. Horrie shook her in a frenzy of growl and saliva. His razor-like teeth pierced deep and high on the reptile's neck and held on. Murchison, in shock, had forgone his other pets and was reaching for Horrie. But the dog was too quick. He backed to the tent flap, shaking and growling for another thirty seconds before, as suddenly as he had begun his frenzied attack, he stopped and let the snake fall from his mouth. It lay on the sand, as limp as a rag doll.

'A bloody good thing!' Featherstone said. 'I can't sleep with that in here!'

Murchison looked aggrieved.

'It had to be,' Gill said, 'there is no way you could have them here with Horrie. He may be a pup, but he must have spent his eight or nine weeks in the desert. This was not his first encounter with a Cleo.'

'He is un-bloody-believable!' Fitzsimmons said. 'I grew up on a farm. I saw brownies and tigers kill quick, strong dogs with one strike. But I never saw anything like that. He *is* so quick and gutsy.'

'Horrie is an Anzac for sure,' Brooker said.

*

Fitzsimmons accompanied a grumpy, but not overly distressed Murchison as he took his tin full of snakes out of the tent and marched into the desert with the aim of letting his pets free.

'The dog wins,' Murchison said. 'He and my babies can't cohabit. Besides, I was getting sick of 'em anyway. But I'll keep one—Doris—for fun and well way from you lot of bloody dyslexics!'

'What did you call us?' Fitzsimmons asked.

'You've all got dyslexia,' Murchison said. 'I know because I have the condition. I can't read properly. I get words and letters mixed up.'

'Why do you say we have this—?'

'Dyslexia? Because you worship D—o—g, instead of G—o—d.'

Fitzsimmons returned to the tent where a few of the others were making a fuss over Horrie's 'performance.' 'Must give him a proper feed,' Fitzsimmons said, picking him up, 'he's earned it.'

Fitzsimmons carried Horrie to the cook's kitchen and gathered some meat scraps. The dog sniffed the offerings, circled the several bits of meat and then one by one buried them in the sand outside. Fitzsimmons remembered Gill's suggestion that Horrie could have belonged to Italians. He found some olive oil in the kitchen and sprinkled it on another piece of meat and offered it to Horrie. The dog sniffed it, walked around it again and then attacked it as if it might run off. Then he easily brought his jaws around it and wolfed it down. He wagged his stump and cocked his head, wanting more. Fitzsimmons found him another sizeable scrap, repeated the oiling up and watched him down it too. He then led a leaping, happy Horrie back to the tent to report his clever thinking about a dog with a possible Italian background needing oil for his meat.

As the afternoon wore on, Horrie was bathed. At first he protested and didn't want it, but as Gill and Moody jollied him into it, with lots of praise and 'What a good boy, Horrie!' and 'Isn't this fun, Horrie!' the dog began to enjoy the attention. Later he watched 'as intently as any human could,' Featherstone wrote to a relative, while Moody and Gill constructed a miniature bunk for Horrie. 'I reckon he knew this was for him,' Featherstone added. 'I might be getting carried away here, but I swear he knew what the lads were saying to each other as they hammered and fitted, fitted and hammered like professional carpenters.'

Featherstone wasn't so sure when Horrie would not settle into the bunk, even when some enticing straw was matted down for him. He wanted to be close to his new set of eight mates. He jumped from bunk to bunk, disturbing readers and writers and those chatting and smoking. At night it was very cold in the desert, dropping from more than 40 degrees to as low as 2 or 3 degrees within a couple of hours after sundown. Horrie waited and sat on the floor near his new sleeping place until it was dark. Then he leapt onto the bunk of a snoring man. At first he was kicked off but on his second attempt at bedding with a human, this time Murchison, he was not dislodged. The former snake-charmer was quite happy to have this hot-water bottle at his feet.

4

BARDIA 'CELEBRATION'

The Ikingi camp was abuzz from 3 to 5 January 1941 with the news that their 6th Division was engaged in the first Allied military operation of the Western Desert campaign. It was against Italian forces and effectively an Australian battle commanded by the experienced, controversial yet genial Lieutenant-General Savige. It was at Bardia, a small town west of Alexandria on the Mediterranean coast of Libya and about 30 kilometres from the Egyptian border. Bulletins filtered into the Ikingi camp from the afternoon of the first day of the engagement and had all members of the Machine Gun Battalion perched over radios and transmitters in several tents. Even Horrie sat near his unit watching for any emotional signs as if he knew what was going on. The scene in the dusty camp was like that of a remote outback mining camp awaiting reports on a far away Grand Final, when sometimes just the scores could cause elation or despondency.

This first conflict for the Australians (or any Allies) in this region brought good reports every few hours. On the morning of 3 January, 6th Division's 16th Brigade attacked and broke through the western face of the defensive perimeter, while the 6th Battalion mounted a diversion in the south. The mere act of starting the battle had hats being thrown high. Two-up games were stopped as men gathered in tents hungry for any snippet. Then it was gleaned that troops of the 17th Australian Brigade had joined the fighting later in the morning to clear the southern portion of the Italian defences. A further cryptic message in code informed the signallers that the 16th Brigade was advancing towards Bardia itself. The Machine Gunners went to bed excited and the nervous energy passed to Horrie who took time to settle in his bunk after barking at everyone, his tail wagging, indicating that he was happy if everyone else was. The news saw him with more pats and attention than even on his first day. Reports from despatches the next day, 4 January, were that Bardia had been captured from the Italians. This brought tremendous reaction at Ikingi. When it was learned that all resistance had been mopped up it was decided that the resting Machine Gun Battalion would march into Alexandria late on the 5th. Murchison was inspired. He spoke of going AWL and joining his countrymen on this 'historic' occasion.

'Save it,' Brooker told him. 'That was a good start but a chickenfeed battle.' He reminded them all for the umpteenth time what a real battle occasion was.

'Try Amiens in northern France in August 1918,' he always told them. 'Monash lined up three armies on the Somme with 102,000 diggers in the middle; the Tommies on his left flank and Canadians on his right. He demanded 400 tanks, 800 planes and 1000 pieces of artillery. We smashed two German armies and dislocated two more inside 48 hours. The enemy never recovered.'

'That's bloody history!' Murchison responded.

'Sure,' Brooker replied, 'but we've just cleaned up one little town on the bloody coast! The first AIF liberated 116 French towns and villages in a hundred days after Amiens in 1918. You must have a perspective. Believe me, we are going to be in for a tough time in this sideshow war. Okay, the Eyeties might be soft, but if Hitler gets worried and sends his crack troops here, well then you'll learn what war's about.'

The results at Bardia came in a few minutes before the late afternoon march into Alexandria began. They were posted in chalk on a board outside the adjutant's office. The 6th Division had lost 130 men with a further 326 wounded. Everyone was concerned that a mate, or a mate of a mate, may have been 'knocked' (killed). Yet the scoreboard, in callous war terms, looked good. More than 40,000 Italian prisoners were taken, along with an impressive cache of arms, rations, equipment and alcohol, with the last item causing mirth among the Rebels. They imagined their fellow gunners hitting the grog that night when they, too, would be raising a glass to the success at Bardia.

Horrie became animated when he saw the men lining up. Moody had trained him already in three short marches to trot along in front of the column. He first tied string to his collar, coaxed him out front and marched with him. After one effort, Horrie knew what was expected of him, and now on this fourth time, he was running around waiting for the Rebels to hurry up and get ready.

Some marvelled at Moody's way with dogs.

'It's nothing,' he said as they sat around on bunks carrying out last-minute polishing of equipment. 'I've taught all the dogs I've had to do tricks.'

When asked if Horrie was his favourite animal, Moody hesitated before answering: 'No, he's not. I once had a red setter called Rudyard that was truly one of God's creatures. The most loveable living thing I ever knew.'

'Was he smart?' Gill asked.

'Super-smart.'

'Smarter than Horrie?'

'Don't know yet,' Moody said with a wry smile, 'but Horrie is a pup with unfathomable potential. You never know. But I will say this: Horrie, at maybe ten weeks, is the cleverest animal, *at that age*, I have ever known.'

'Hitler reckons the German shepherd is the most intelligent canine of all,' Gill commented.

'He would, wouldn't he?' Moody replied, 'he's got them. But a lot depends on diet, environment and the attitude of the owner in opening up the dog's mind. Brains in dogs, cats and humans are pretty well the same. If they are exercised and tested and pushed and rewarded, they will grow and develop. They must be given lots of respect, affection and communication. Deprive them, or leave them to wallow without communication, and their minds will not expand; they will wither and rot.'

'I agree with the respect bit,' Murchison proffered, 'I respect my pets...'

The others laughed.

'No, no, Murchie's right,' Moody said. 'Watch Horrie. Because Horrie is so clever, he is also very sensitive. We learned early when he was catching lizards that he did not like being laughed at. Just be careful and don't tease him. He has my permission to take a chunk out of your leg if you do.'

The others howled Moody down and threw socks at him.

'Just mark my words,' he warned with a grin.

*

Lieutenant 'Big Jim' Hewitt, the Gunners' broad-shouldered officer, bellowed to Brooker and spick-and-span Corporal Featherstone, whose boots were like mirrors, to hurry the Rebels out on parade. They formed part of the last unit to line up with their platoon. Horrie darted in and out of the lines as Lieutenant Hewitt, accompanied by Featherstone, inspected each man from his kit to his boots. Horrie was joined by a stray dog and it was treated with barely disguised disdain for being with *his* platoon. Horrie stood or sat just to the rear and out of eyeshot of Hewitt and Featherstone, and his interest in the shortcomings of each man seemed intent. The other dog sniffed around, less enamoured with the inspection, but nevertheless staying close by Horrie. This went on for 15 minutes. Another platoon marched by to a steady sergeant's cry of 'left—right—left . . .' Horrie watched it and wanted his team to move off too. He barked. The other dog did the same. In his exhilaration, Horrie came up behind the preoccupied Featherstone and cocked a leg on his boots. The other dog, also perhaps miffed that there were no trees in the desert, followed suit. Featherstone did not notice, but the soldiers on parade did. A titter ran through the ranks. The second effort by the stray dog brought outright laughter. Big Jim Hewitt and Featherstone wheeled around.

'Steady the men,' Hewitt ordered Featherstone.

'Quiet!' Featherstone bellowed, oblivious to what had happened.

The men laughed again.

'What's so funny?' Hewitt said. 'Each man stand like an oak; an *oak*, I say!'

'That's what Horrie thought the corporal was, sir!' Fitzsimmons called out.

That brought a roar from the ranks.

'I think Horrie wet your . . . um—' someone began but was interrupted by Fitzsimmons, as quick as ever, who called: 'Your appetite, sir . . . whet your appetite for the march.'

'Any more comment and you'll be in the brig for a week!' Hewitt snapped in reference to the camp jail.

Horrie was pleased to hear the order to 'march out.' He dashed to the head of the column without being instructed. He trotted along, keeping a few metres in front of the platoon, and occasionally looking back. Horrie only deviated after about 500 metres when he spotted some young Arab boys trailing to the side of the platoon. He growled and looked like he might bolt for them. But several sharp cries of 'No, Horrie! No!' from the ranks, and particularly Moody, had the dog returning to his straight-ahead movement.

After five kilometres of slogging in the heat on the 30 kilometre route to Alexandria, a sergeant called: 'Okay, halt and smoko, ten minutes, lads!'

Six Arab boys in raggy clothes, whom only Horrie had been able to spot in the distance, sprang from the dunes offering food and drink including dates, watermelon, dark grapes, eggs, meats and Bedouin-made lemonade. Horrie growled and snapped at them, causing a hurried retreat.

'He hates wogs, doesn't he?' someone observed.

'They probably kicked him around wherever he was in his first weeks,' Gill said. 'Why else would he be so dark with them? He has never so much as yelped at a digger, except for one notable shit.'

The urchins kept a wary eye on Horrie and mingled with the soldiers at the other end of the platoon as they slouched and smoked.

'Very clean,' they informed the gunners, holding up bruised-looking apples. 'Washy today, washy today.'

The soldiers were wary and even more so with the clever use of phrases the boys hoped would resonate with the Australians: 'Fresh! Hygiene!'

The food was inspected and mostly rejected. The bitter lemonade was bought by a few thirsty men wishing to supplement their water ration in the heat, which had climbed to more than 40 degrees. Horrie took the moment to move about ten metres from the platoon to do his business. He used his paws to cover his deposit with sand. The boys laughed as he buried it in a few inches. They pointed: 'Dog, very hygiene! Dog, Aussie dog, very hygiene!'

Some of the soldiers laughed. Horrie looked around at everyone, unhappy at being the centre of ridicule. He fixed on his Arab tormentors. Then, like a shark intent on one victim, he tore at a boy, who ran off. It brought more mirth to the platoon. Horrie tracked him and then flew at his leg, collected his trouser and shook it as he had Cleo, tearing the fabric and shearing it off. The boy stumbled and fell, kicking at the aggressive Horrie, who seemed to be in a frenzy. Moody and Gill ran to the scene fearing Horrie might do some serious damage. Moody called him to heel. At the second command, the dog gave up his would-be victim.

Moody led him over to the Rebels. Gill and Murchison patted him, calming him down. They offered him a drink from his own designated wooden bowl. He lapped it up, intermittently looking up to watch and emit low guttural sounds just below a growl at one of the Arab boys, who all kept a wary distance.

'What did I say about respecting him?' Moody asked.

'You're so right,' Featherstone observed. 'Fearless little beggar, with a certain dignity.'

'He is so sensitive to the difference between just playing with him, which we do, and making fun of him,' Gill said. 'Don't you just love him? We *must* make his status official. He is already really one of us.'

The others nodded their agreement. Horrie wagged his tail, causing Featherstone to smile and to repeat earlier observations: 'I always feel he knows what we are saying.'

They marched on another five kilometres and approached an Arab village. Hewitt ordered them to 'march to attention,' which saw rifles sloped, shoulders square and strides long and in step. The men stopped nattering to each other. It was meant to impress the village. All of its members seemed to have turned out to see them. The young Arab boys continued to be curious and cheeky.

'C'mon, digger,' one called, 'eyes front. No girls here!'

'At ease,' another cried, much to the laughter of others.

Murchison could never resist some interplay. '*Seieda*, George,' he called, using the Arab salutation and the name the diggers had for all Arabs, among others. The boy replied, 'Good day, Wog!'

This drew laughs from the platoon ranks. Murchison did not like being trumped. Other boys were encouraged.

'Going to Alexandria, eh, digger? We got really pretty girls for you. Sexeeee!'

'Where, George?' Murchison asked.

'Anfousia Quarter. Between fort and palace. Sailors stay there. We show you. Nice area. Nice cafe.'

'Very clean,' another boy interjected, 'very hygiene!'

All the boys cackled at that.

'We take you!' they almost cried in chorus.

'Don't worry, Murchie,' Brooker said, 'we are going to that quarter. I've heard of a good cafe there.'

'Forget the bloody brothels, son,' Moody said. 'Alexandria is one of the great historical cities in the world. Founded by Alexander the Great in 331 BC.'

'Yeah, the hookers are quite ancient, Murchie,' Fitzsimmons commented, drawing laughs.

'How come you know your history?' Featherstone asked Moody. 'You study it at school or uni or something?'

'No. I did science subjects, although I wish I'd studied history. There were very good teachers at school.'

'Which school?'

'Scotch College.'

'That's strange,' Fitzsimmons chipped in.

'Why?'

'Thought you'd be at Beer College.'

The exhausted platoon reached Alexandria's outskirts and was surprised at its size, the big population and the very cosmopolitan look of the people. Some ignored them as just another bunch of foreign soldiers. Others waved and smiled. The Rebels noted the lack of high-rise buildings as they reached the tree-lined city centre, Mohammed Ali Square, with its large equestrian monument. The solid buildings were European in style with the Church of St Mark's prominent. A halt was called due to the large number of buses and cars. Hewitt ordered them to break ranks and be back at the corner in four hours when they would be trucked back to camp. The Rebels followed Brooker to the Anfousia district with its narrow streets of cafes. Murchison was first to notice exotic women on some of the balconies and he nearly bumped into the others while craning his neck. Scantily clad women winked, wiggled their hips, waved, smiled from behind thin veils and called:

'Come on, Aussie; we give you good time; we make love . . . good beer too . . .'

'How do they know we're Aussie?' Featherstone asked.

'The slouch hats and uniforms for a start,' Fitzsimmons said, and added, 'and some of them look like they might remember Brooker from the Great War.'

They reached a cafe called The Moroccan. Horrie was not allowed in. Featherstone volunteered to stay outside with him. The others entered the large, dimly lit, smoke-filled cafe where an Arab ensemble band, each man wearing a red fez, was playing music. They were struck by a heatwave of mixed smells; of beer, sweat, incense and cigar smoke. Almost all the tables were filled with military patrons from a variety of nations, including New Zealanders, South Africans, Free French, British, Americans and some Africans.

'Over 'ere, Dig!' an Australian called and chairs were organised for the Rebels, who found themselves cheek-by-jowl with British soldiers ('Tommies'), who were not thrilled at the new arrivals. They crowded into a packed room. The hum of conversation, punctuated by loud laughing, almost drowned out the band. Not even a snake-charmer could gain attention, except from Murchison, as a large asp uncoiled itself to the piped music of a cross-legged Arab wearing multicoloured coat, pants and fez.

'That's Joseph,' Fitzsimmons observed, just as the room fell silent as a curvaceous dark-haired beauty began to create an exotic dance around the snake, which made his gradual elevation to the music. The veiled big-eyed dancer, wearing green shorts and a shirt tied beneath her ample breasts, gyrated her hips.

'Jeez!' Fitzsimmons said as the asp coiled up. 'I'd get it up for her too!'

'Shut up!' a British soldier called. 'You rude Aussie git!'

'Nah,' Fitzsimmons responded, 'guess you'd have trouble, Tommy, eh?'

A few comments, mostly good-natured, flew between the two groups of soldiers. A polite Arab waiter asked if the Rebels wanted their hats hung up. Some removed their head-gear.

'Here,' Murchison said, 'hang this up too.'

In the darkness and the smoke and with several hats in his hand, the Arab waiter did not realise he had been handed Doris, Murchison's last snake. The Arab shrieked as he tried to dislodge the reptile from around his neck.

He fell back onto the table of British soldiers, upsetting it and sending beers and food spilling to the floor. A Tommy flew at Murchison. Within seconds there was an all-in brawl.

Outside, Featherstone threw away a cigarette.

'Stay right here, Horrie mate,' he ordered and rushed into the cafe, where there was chaos. About 30 men tangled with each other while the other soldiers formed a rough semicircle watching the all-in tussle. Wild punches were thrown by both sides, with only a few landing as all tables were upturned, glasses were broken and the tumbling, wrestling, punching mass swirled close to the stage, causing the band to disperse. Murchison was the wildest fighter of the lot, flailing at every Tommy in or out of striking distance. By contrast, Moody prowled the perimeter of the 'ring' and ducked and weaved. Then he lined up opponents who stumbled in his direction for a big right-hand swinging punch. He was all method and cold intent, while avoiding being caught up in wrestling. He hit two Tommies square on the jaw, leaving them motionless.

In the rush of bodies, the snake-charmer had lost his reptile. Then Horrie waddled into the cafe. He spotted both Murchison's snake Doris and the disturbed asp. He danced around them, barking and uncertain which one to attack. Meanwhile the Arab cafe owners tried to stop the brawl, which was not an uncommon occurrence in this quarter. The management called the police, who were close by. With cries of 'Police! Police!' the various soldier groups bolted for the doors and open windows. The Rebels continued some push-and-shove with the Tommies but soon were careering down a side alley as they heard police whistles, yelling and car sirens. Horrie bounced along with them, wagging his stump. He had missed snaring another reptile victim, but he was happy to be with his squad after the fracas.

'That was great!' a breathless Murchison said, wiping away blood from the corner of his mouth. 'We've only been in Alexandria twenty bloody minutes! What a place! Love it!'

'Everyone is accounted for,' Brooker said, looking around at all the Rebels and then down at Horrie. Murchison expressed interest in the prostitutes but the others suggested that they have a 'beer and a feed' before any other 'adventures.' They found a quiet cafe a few streets away and settled down to some modest fare.

By chance they had chosen a cafe bar frequented by prostitutes, who had meals there before their nocturnal duties. Two stunning, long-limbed, very dark-skinned African women came in and found a corner seat without even batting an eyelid at the Rebels. Murchison did everything to catch their attention, short of sitting with them.

'They're not interested in you or any of us in here,' Brooker explained. 'Do you think they are going to flirt off-duty? No way! They want peace and quiet away from the terrible mob of sweaty blokes from all the nations on earth before they switch to vaudeville later in their houses of ill repute.'

Murchison fondled his beer and picked at his food, his eyes darting in the direction of the Africans. He seemed unconvinced but confused that his wordless charm and boyish good looks were having no impact.

'Look, mate,' Brooker added, 'you can have a go at them when they finish their meals. Let 'em be now. They'll let you know if they are interested, when *they* are ready. Not before. Remember, this is their turf, not ours.'

'I don't think I've ever seen anything like them,' Murchison said in whispered awe. 'The bodies on them! The arses!'

The others laughed.

Murchison kept watching and when the girls reached for their purses, he pounced. He sidled to their table, sat down and chatted. He paid their meal bill and asked if they would like drinks. In a faltering, French-tinged lilt, the one he fancied most smiled a crater of white teeth, and said: 'Come with us? We have the best wines at our place, okay?'

With that Murchison took the girls to the Rebels and introduced them and Horrie, who was sitting close to Moody waiting for table scraps. Moody leaned across to Fitzsimmons and whispered: 'You'd better go with him and ride shotgun. Never know what will happen to the kid.'

'They'll fleece him for sure,' Fitzsimmons said under his breath and stubbing his cigarette. 'Better do my duty.' He winked at Moody and then yelled to Murchison: 'Hey, mate, mind if I join you?'

5

REVENGE

Horrie was roaming around the Ikingi camp at breakfast time visiting his many friends, for almost the entire battalion had taken to this most outstanding little character. But there was always the odd soldier who was indifferent to pets, and a couple who were hostile. One was Sergeant Ross 'Gerry' Fitzgerald, the most hated man at Ikingi, who was only tolerated by a few cowering sycophants from his platoon, who laughed along with his every mindless, sneering aside. He liked to brawl and was known for his bullying, especially of the rank and file, whom he delighted in attacking for the smallest detail, especially if they refused to drink with him after hours. Fitzgerald was a sly grogger through the day and by the end of daylight, he was often morose and ready for a 'top up' with the nearest soldier who dared to be near him. This particular morning, Horrie innocently padded his way into Fitzgerald's tent. He approached the grunting, snoring man on his bunk and tried to lick his face. The big man awoke to the saliva-filled passion, swung off the bunk swearing and kicking at Horrie. The dog sidestepped him but was cornered. Fitzgerald lashed at him again, this time connecting with the dog's upper left leg. Horrie let out a yelp, and scrambled for the tent flap with Fitzgerald stumbling after him trying to kick him again.

At that moment, a hung-over Murchison, his arm slung over Fitzsimmons' shoulder, returned from Alexandria. After a night of carousing, they had hitched a truck ride back to camp at dawn. They saw a limping Horrie scuttle from the tent, with Fitzgerald following and yelling abuse: 'Fuckin' little wog dog! Next time I'll fuckin' kick you to death!!'

Fitzgerald wandered back into his tent. Murchison was intent on taking the big man on, but was restrained by Fitzsimmons, just as Moody and Brooker came out of the Rebels' tent. Moody saw the forlorn, limping Horrie and asked what had happened. The four of them inspected the dog's leg. It already had swelling, but it was pronounced 'unbroken.' Murchison, irritable and ready for action, had to be physically restrained by the other three, who dragged him back to their tent. They settled him down while Featherstone and Brooker bathed the sorry-looking Horrie and applied a bandage to his bruised leg. He loved the attention but refused to cheer up, his little tail motionless. Brooker surmised that Horrie knew the attention would not be so generous if he was his usual cheerful self.

'If you take that bastard Gerry on,' Moody said to Murchison, 'that will be the end of Horrie. We'll have to let him go.'

'Yeah, worse,' Fitzsimmons added, 'that ugly bugger will shoot him, I swear!'

'I want to bash his head in!' Murchison said.

'Sober up, kid,' Moody said. 'You'd be on a serious charge for tackling Gerry. He's a sergeant-of-the-guard, you know. Just about the last of the NCOs who you could cross that way. There'd be hell to pay.'

'Yeah, that's right,' Gordie said, interested enough to look up from the radio set he was working on. 'Snotty Johns happened to mention to someone that Gerry had bad breath. Gerry found out and threw him in the brig for a week. The bastard has rotten BO as well, but please don't let him know I said so!'

'Gerry should be nicknamed Fitzeverything,' Fitzsimmons said.

'Meaning?' Moody asked.

'Fitz means "the bastard of."'

'So your antecedents somewhere in the past must have branched off as "the bastard of Simon" or a name like that?'

'Yes, but I prefer it came from *Fits of laughter*.'

The Rebels had a conference. Moody thought it was his responsibility to 'square off' for Horrie. Some suggestions, such as two of them jumping him in the latrine, were rejected.

'Gotta be done at night so he can't recognise the man committing the assault,' Brooker suggested.

Moody thought while the others argued, then he said: 'Got it! We find out when he is next on guard duty at night. Then we hit him.' He looked up at all the expectant faces. 'I mean, *I'll* hit him.'

'You?' Murchison said with a trace of disdain. 'I admire your pluck, cobber, but Gerry's about a head taller.'

'And nearly twice as heavy!' Shegog added as he set up his easel for his portrait painting. 'He's a brute. You can't beat him in a fight.'

'Correct,' Moody said, 'but this must not be a fight. He must be hit once, maybe twice, by surprise in the dark.'

The others were stunned by his clinical precision, and determination.

After a prolonged silence, Featherstone asked: 'Won't he recognise you even at night?'

'Don't think so,' Moody with a sly grin. 'He's a vain prick. He can't see too well without his glasses. I'm told the bully-boy sometimes doesn't wear them, especially in pitch black when you often can't see out here anyway.'

Two nights later, the word circulated that Fitzgerald would be in command of guard duty at the isolated main guard post some 50 metres from the camp. The area was open to anyone straying into the camp and had attracted Arabs who couldn't resist stealing. In centuries-old desert tribal law this could result in a severe penalty, even death. But foreigners were considered fair game for pilfering. The Arabs were rarely deterred by the presence of guards at the perimeter of the widespread camp of tents, and youths and young boys in particular were cunning and audacious in slipping past guards by day and night.

Moody slipped out of the Rebels' tent just before 2 a.m. and walked a wide circuit of the tents. He approached the main guard-house, which was a makeshift hut with a corrugated iron roof. Moody pulled on a black face mask and crept to within 30 metres of the hut. At 2 a.m., he could just make out someone, probably Fitzgerald, leaving the main guard-house with a torch for his ritual visit to all the camps' six outer-lying posts, which were spaced about 50 metres apart. Moody, heart pounding, followed the source of the bobbing light and moved up to within a few metres of the striding Fitzgerald, who stopped when he thought he heard movement. He pointed his torch. Its light fell a few metres from Moody, who had to be sure this was the target he was aiming at.

'Who goes there?' Moody said in a rumbling voice, disguising his own.

'The sergeant-of-the-guard!' Fitzgerald replied, adjusting his glasses and reaching for a holstered revolver.

'Sergeant Fitzgerald?' Moody asked.

'Yes!'

Moody rushed forward and from a side-on position swung his right fist hard at the big man's jaw. Fitzgerald moved his head towards his attacker and Moody's fist collected the sergeant's bulbous nose. He slumped to his knees with a groan. Moody was away. Seconds before Fitzgerald had stumbled back to the main guard-house to raise the alarm, Moody was back in the Rebels' tent.

'Did you get him?' Murchison asked, as all the Rebels waited for his response under the uncertain light of one kerosene lamp. Moody did not reply. Instead he took off his boots and flexed his right hand. He sauntered over to Horrie, who was off his bunk greeting his favourite Rebel. Moody bent down and placed his right hand under the dog's nose. Horrie sniffed and then licked a little trickle of blood from a cut on the knuckle. Moody patted his head. The dog wagged his tail. The kerosene light was doused as movement was heard outside.

'I take it that's a "yes"?' Murchison asked.

'Might see the result in the morning,' Moody said as shouting commenced outside. Several of the Rebels sniggered as one of the camp's searchlights snaked over their tent.

'Must be a wog thief,' Fitzsimmons said. 'Bastard! Bet he's got bad breath and body odour as well.'

The others laughed and settled to sleep despite the commotion outside the tent as a small party prowled the grounds inside and out of the Ikingi camp in search of an assailant of the sergeant-of-the-guard.

*

On parade the next morning, the Rebels could hardly contain their enjoyment of the retribution for the injury done to one of their own. As Hewitt announced that a 'cowardly blow' had been struck to the sergeant-of-the-guard 'in the night,' all battalion eyes fell on Fitzgerald, who sported an elaborate bandage wrapped around his head and covering his nose. It was not enough to conceal two of the blackest eyes the soldiers had ever seen. Both were just slits embedded in dark red and brown puffiness. The grumpy Fitzgerald was in a darker mood than anyone had ever seen him before.

'Jesus!' Murchison whispered to Moody in the line in front of him. 'What did you use, a bloody sledgehammer?!' Moody raised his right arm slowly, and flexed his middle finger. The others could not suppress laughs.

Hewitt swung around to face the minor disturbance.

'Quiet on parade!' he bellowed. 'This is a very serious matter indeed. May well be a court martial! It may see the assailant being sent back home after a long jail term.'

'How do you know it wasn't a wog, sir?' someone called from the ranks. 'They can be vicious, sir!'

'I don't answer such insolent interjections, Private Young! But this once I shall reply that we know it was not a . . . a . . . um . . . local native. The assailant asked the sergeant's name. Therefore he and I conclude it was, *it just had to be*, one of you.' Hewitt paused and added: 'We'd like the offender to step forward, now.'

No one moved.

'Permission to speak, sir,' another soldier called.

'Yes, Private Oliver . . . speak.'

'These wogs—er . . . Bedouin, sir, are pretty smart. They do call out names—'

'Stop there, Private!' Hewitt interjected. 'We *know* it was one of you and no stone will be left unturned until we find the culprit.'

'But, sir, what would be the motive for hitting such a nice man?' Oliver called.

'Enough!' Hewitt yelled as he took several paces towards the private. 'You will report to my office forthwith. Each tent will be inspected by me and Sergeant Fitzgerald this morning.'

A half-hour later, Hewitt and the sergeant entered the Rebels' tent. Fitzgerald's eyes, such as they were, met those of all the members, who stared back. Horrie's body had a slight tremor. He growled from atop his bunk as he kept a steady gaze directed at the sergeant.

'Now, Horrie,' Moody said, 'be nice to the nice sergeant.'

'Sergeant Brooker,' Hewitt said, 'were any of your men AWL at any time last night?'

'Absolutely not, sir. Every man, and Horrie, was present and accounted for right through the night from lights out at 10 p.m., sir.'

'Don't be so indignant, Sergeant. Your men have the worst record in the camp for AWL offences.'

'Sir?' Fitzsimmons said, stepping forward and saluting comically. 'I can vouch for the veracity of the sergeant's words, sir.'

'Oh, how Private Fitzsimmons?'

'I can say honestly that he tucked each and every one of us in, sir; always does.'

This comment created barely contained glee from the others. Fitzgerald looked set to explode.

'Shut up, Private!' Hewitt snapped and added, 'This had better be true.'

Hewitt left the tent. Fitzgerald lingered with a menacing body posture.

'I know it was one of you arseholes!' he said, glaring at Murchison. Horrie was again shaking with concern. Moody restrained him.

'Our little mascot doesn't seem to like you, Sergeant,' Moody said, eyeballing Fitzgerald. 'Someone kicked him in the leg the other day. I suppose you wouldn't know who?'

'I couldn't give a stuff about that little mongrel!' Fitzgerald snarled.

'When we find out who *did* kick him,' Moody added, 'we might give him a couple of shiners like you have, Sergeant.'

'And if I find out if one of you—' Fitzgerald hissed.

'Don't threaten my men!' Brooker said stepping forward to face Fitzgerald. 'Or our mascot!'

Fitzgerald stormed out fuming and cursing under his breath. When he was well away, several Rebel fists went in the air. Some shook hands with Moody. Others patted and hugged Horrie, who settled down.

'Revenge of the Wog Dog,' Shegog remarked as he arranged his paintbrushes, 'so sweet when served cold!' He glanced at the dog. 'Horrie, old mate, today I think the subject should be you.'

*

The camp received a further boost when British and Australian forces attacked Tobruk and captured 25,000

Italians, along with 208 guns and 87 tanks, in a comprehensive victory. Churchill then ordered British General Wavell to capture the port city of Benghazi, Libya's second-largest city, where the 6th Division would be prominent. The war had started well for the Allies, particularly the diggers.

6

THE REBELS MOVE OUT

The battalion had plenty to celebrate with the news on 6 February 1941 that its fellow soldiers had defeated the Italians and taken Benghazi. Several of the Rebels took off to celebrate in Alexandria again. It was a useful excuse for going AWL to avoid the hard training that had gone on in January and into February. Desert exercises were mainly boring, arduous long marches, featuring the use of prismatic compass and map reading. Moody and Gill continued their own training routines and sidestepped tagging along with the gunners, arguing that their jobs would be different, solo efforts on their motorbikes. But once or twice even they were press-ganged into night operations where there would be long carries of the guns. Selected gun positions had to be located, always with the ubiquitous and vital compass, and the Vickers would be set up. Here the despatch riders doubled as forward scouts in the pitch black and often freezing nights. Moody and Gill enjoyed the extra challenge of bouncing and roaring along in the desert with just their headlights to guide them. The conditions were harsh and made worse when there were sand and dust storms that burnt skin and eyes and parched throats.

Despite these exercises, there was still more down-time for the signallers, and the Rebels grew restless with the wait. Murchison annoyed everyone, especially in the dead of night when he played with his pistol and accidentally, or so he claimed, let it off. His disturbing game came to an abrupt halt on 16 February when Private J. P. Ryan was accidentally killed by another soldier. He was buried with a guard of honour in the Alexandria Cemetery when half the battalion turned out to pay their respects.

'I've learned the lesson,' Murchison told Brooker, 'thank God without killing anybody.'

The Rebels were caught up in plenty of scraps in Cairo, similar to the one on their first venture to Alexandria, but two events sobered them up once more. One occurred on 21 March when HQ Company Sergeant-Major J. H. Trice was killed in a taxi accident. All the Rebels had been on hair-raising taxi rides but this loss caused them to be more circumspect, often blasting or threatening the drivers if they became too reckless. The other just-as-sobering occurrence was the contracting of venereal disease by some of the men after brothel adventures in Cairo. Murchison, the most careless and carefree of the Rebels in sampling the whores of the red-light districts, was not too worried at first, but when he learned that syphilis had been so bad for a couple of soldiers that they had been sent home, he was far more cautious, as were the others, about wearing protection and avoiding the worst spots. The authorities had been ruthless about policing the brothel areas such as Wasser. This Cairo district had gained legendary status early in 1915 when a group of the first Anzacs burnt down a brothel and beat up all the local pimps. This was in reprisals for much thieving of wallets while the soldiers and troopers were preoccupied with enjoying themselves, and for the high preponderance of venereal disease contracted in Wasser. The officers 26 years later were determined not to let a repeat happen in World War II. But no matter how hard they clamped down with punishment, most of the soldiers still managed to carouse in the most notorious areas. In the back of many soldiers' minds was the thought that they had better have some 'fun' before the war hotted up for them.

*

Sergeant Brooker had been accurate in his assessment that the German war machine would not sit by and let their partner Italy be swept aside in the Mediterranean region. The Italians had invaded Greece a few months earlier on 28 October 1940. The Greeks had done well in defeating that first attack, and then a further Italian counterattack in March 1941. That was enough for the German dictator

Adolf Hitler. He and his generals devised Operation Marita, which began on 6 April, when the bulk of the Greek army was on the Albanian border, from which the Italians were trying to enter Greece. German troops invaded through Bulgaria, creating a second front. British Commonwealth troops, including Australians, were to be sent to Greece to bolster the defences.

The first sign for the Rebels that something was 'on' for them was the stepping up of inspections by Brooker of signals gear. He had never been overbearing before but now he was harassing the sloppy members of the group. The second sign came when the platoon's two best despatch riders, Moody and Gill, received two gleaming new British Norton motorcycles, with their four-speed gearboxes. They began tuning the air-cooled engines. Moody took his bike apart to see if there were any advances or changes in design, and he found several. The two daredevils soon worked out the roughest course possible for a race with four other riders. An enthusiastic crowd gathered to watch a dash over an eight kilometre course across gullies and small ravines, and along a couple of precarious ridges. For once in the camp, two-up betting aggregates were topped by those for the outcome of the race. Gill and Moody were neck and neck in the straight back to the camp when Gill's bike broke down and Moody romped in ahead of the next rider by a hundred metres. Shegog was injured when his bike toppled off a ridge; he ended up on crutches and out of the war for the moment.

The third sign of the Machine Gun Battalion joining the Battle of Greece, as it was soon known, came when Moody biked with Gill into Alexandria to buy film for his camera. The Greek proprietor, Jimmy Stavros, who spoke English, elicited at first frowns, then enlightenment when he said: 'Run out, sorry, lads, but you'll be able to buy plenty in Athens.'

'Athens?' Moody and Gill said in chorus.

'Sure,' Stavros replied, 'didn't you know? The Brits are sending about 60,000 to fight in Greece. About 60 per cent will be you Anzacs; the rest Brits.'

'How do you know this, Jimmy?' Moody asked.

'Got a relative in the Greek Cabinet,' he said, dropping his voice but pleased with the information he was passing on. 'You'll be fully equipped with 60 and 25 pounder guns. An armoured brigade will be going. It's big! You can imagine how the Greeks in the know feel. Gives us hope.'

Later Brooker confirmed what just about all of the Ikingi camp knew: they were indeed being shipped from Alexandria to Piraeus, the port at Athens. The Rebels were facing a few realities as they hurried to write letters to make the last post to Australia. Their messages were not alarmist. Instead, warmth and love flowed through the ink-stained and pencil scribbled lines as each man faced an abrupt sense of mortality. The German machine had a formidable reputation and each soldier knew that the odds of them ever returning home had changed overnight. Most relished the thought of 'getting some action at last.' Almost all were thrilled to be leaving the boring, hot confines of their remote waterless outpost. But the thought of German bombers, ships, paratroopers and those infamous, experienced, hard-helmeted troops was sobering. Right through the camp now was an electrified sense of preparation as machine guns were tested with their ear-splitting *rat-tat-tat, rat-tat-tat.* This sound was supplemented by the seemingly continuous testing of rifles and revolvers by all carriers of these weapons. But the sound that out-blasted them all was the throaty roar of the motorcycles as they sent dust trails through the desert when Moody, Gill and others raced daily and went through the roughest exercises they could create. They skylarked by sending their bikes high and in doing the odd trick, including a somersault over a dry wadi, which Moody and Gill had planned over several weeks. They also perfected the less problematic 'hanger,' where they would do a handstand on the handlebars. One slip in such acts would see bike or rider or both a broken wreck. Officers did not countenance such performances and the stunts were carried out well away from the camp. Yet there was some method in their madness for both men knew that in war they would be asked to take risks on the front. Knowing the limits of the bikes and themselves was more than a useful mental 'track' or preparation for what they would face. They regarded it all as necessary mental and physical training.

*

The biggest concern for the Rebels was what to do with Horrie. In eight weeks he had become an integral part of the squad and a feature of the entire battalion. His collar featured its colours, as did his dish, painted bunk and a tennis ball that had been presented to him. Horrie had put on weight for he was a favourite of the cooks in the kitchen, who normally had only a few close mates in the ranks. Moody continued to teach him tricks and 'duties.' His prime job was to guard all the equipment in and out of the tent, especially from prowling Arabs, who filtered in and around the camp day and night. When a Rebel took him outside their tent and said, 'Watch!' in a commanding voice, the dog took the command seriously and never strayed, even when another animal wandered within his range of smell or sight. He could be left for hours at a time. His second and equally useful duty was to run messages. Moody trained him by taking him to the destination, including the transport and equipment depot, which was the camp workshop, where everything from nuts and bolts to lighting rods and radio parts were found. Moody introduced him to a mate at the depot, Ron Ford, who would make a fuss of him and offer chocolate. The 'game' would begin with Horrie taking a message tied to his collar to Ron from ten metres, then twenty metres and then out of sight. After half an hour, Horrie understood that with the command 'Take it to Ron,' he would dash from the Rebels' tent to the depot with the message. Similarly, if Ron had a query he would attach it to the willing Horrie with the command 'Take it to the Rebels.'

'If that little bloke had wings,' Ford observed, 'he'd be better than any carrier pigeon.'

The third major feature of Horrie's repertoire was a lesson for the Rebels rather than the dog. On occasions, he would sit and bark at the sky, his outsized ears erect and pointing in one direction. When none of the Rebels reacted, he darted about and then stopped, his head steady, his bark excited and his growls deep and long. After this happened a few times, Moody noted that it coincided with a plane flying overhead up to two minutes after Horrie began his antics. Moody drew the other Rebels' attention to this phenomenon one day when they were assembling their equipment outside the tent.

'Our littlest Anzac is an early warning system!' Murchison said. 'We just gotta take him with us!'

All the Rebels agreed. They hatched several plans that fell through and in the end decided to smuggle him in Moody's pack. Moody's equipment was shared in the packs of the others, which left plenty of wriggle room for the dog. But it was stifling hot for the more than 30 kilometre march and train ride under a harsh sun to the port at Alexandria. A hole was cut in the side near the top of the pack. Horrie was a twitch of excitement at the heightened activity in the camp. He knew something was up and he looked anxious. Each Rebel would drop to his haunches and tell him: 'Everything is okay, mate. You are one of us. You're coming with us.'

Moody, the dog whisperer, now had one of the toughest canine assignments in training Horrie to get in the pack and stay quiet. The dog looked forlorn at the prospect of this new 'trick.' He didn't refuse it but he wriggled in the confinement in a mild protest. Moody went through the routine in two stretches of 20 minutes each, spaced several hours apart. Horrie was placed, rear-end first, into the pack. He would squirm himself into position so that his little set-upon face and snout would poke from the hole. Then Moody would trudge a hundred metres and back, giving plenty of praise and encouragement. By the end of this exercise, Horrie was ready, although man and dog could not envisage what imponderables they might face en route. The plan was to sneak him on board the ship taking them to Greece, a journey of two days and nights. Once there, the Rebels would hatch plan two on how to keep him unseen when smuggled aboard.

On the last night before the march, a greater concern enveloped the Rebel tent as each man had trouble sleeping. Their minds churned over coming possibilities. Brooker's remark that they had 'nothing to fear but fear itself' helped a fraction as he reminded them that he had come through the Great War unscathed, but his accompanying homily was less comforting: 'If you get knocked you will know nothing, so what's the point in worrying? There is no pain after death.'

That blunt comment had some reaching for pen and paper to say more poignant things to loved ones with the thought that this might just be the last letter that ever reached home. But sentimentality gave several of them 'writers' block' and the nervous anticipation caused many to enjoy less than their normal quota of seven hours sleep. In the middle of a cold night they boiled tea and chatted.

Horrie, alert as ever when the Rebels were in discussion, wandered to each bunk offering a lick and a nuzzle of solace, which would in return lead to a warm pat or cuddle. The Rebels swore that he sensed their feelings on such occasions. In the dead of night, when the unknown played on dwelling minds, there was just a whiff of fear in the tent. The mood was broken when Brooker, with ecclesiastical soberness, commented that it was the Rebels' last night in the land of milk and honey.

'That's if you bring your own cows and bees,' Fitzsimmons quipped. It was a fitting enough joke at 3 a.m. for them to attempt to slumber for the last few hours before the dawn.

*

Horrie, anticipating something was afoot, was awake first as the warm fingers of dawn crept over the barren camp at Ikingi on 6 April, the day the Germans began the Battle of Greece by invading that country and Yugoslavia, making the date even more significant. Breakfast was rushed. Horrie seemed miffed that the mobile kitchen was being packed up before he could acquire the usual scraps. The camp was a cacophonous mix of trucks being warmed up, orders being barked and movement everywhere. Men were heaving packs onto backs, slinging rifles over shoulders and placing machine-gun parts in 'coffins,' the unfortunate word for the long bags that held the raison d'être of this particular battalion. Horrie moved from Rebel to Rebel, seeking reassurance that he would not be left out of this 'event.' Moody and Gill kept watch on him and, when he looked ready to dash to the front of the battalion, they warned him not to leave.

'This is the moment of your great disappearing trick, my little mate,' Gill said, scratching the dog's spine.

The Rebels heard the order for them to fall in on parade. Moody looked at Horrie and then the bag.

'Sorry, my little friend, but this is it,' he said. He pointed to the bag. Horrie looked crestfallen as he sauntered over to it. One last pleading look from him was ignored by Moody, who patted him and helped him in.

The thousand men of the 1st Machine Gun Battalion lined up as straight and stiff as terracotta soldiers. Officers began the inspection of each man. The chief officer, Colonel Poulson, who had replaced Hewitt (who was ill with an unspecified fever), was as tall and commanding but with a grim mien that bothered the Rebels. The dog-in-a-kit plan now depended on Horrie remaining silent. The colonel stepped along the line, his eyes darting over each man and his kit. Every ten soldiers or so, he would demand that a soldier remove his kit, sit it at his feet and open it. This act had the Rebels sweating in the early morning heat and glancing at each other. The colonel and his entourage of three other officers arrived at Murchison, who was next to Moody.

'You could be less slovenly, Private!' the colonel observed. 'Kit, down!'

Murchison obeyed with a nervous glance at Moody.

'What are you looking at Private "AWL" Moody for? He can't be responsible for your appearance.' The colonel paused then added the sharp instruction: 'Kit, open!'

Moody felt a little wriggle from Horrie and prayed he would not bark at the unfriendly commands. The sun was becoming hotter each minute. The soldiers had been stationary for half an hour during this arduous routine that had become a trial for every Rebel as they feared Horrie would be discovered. The colonel looked down at the opened bag. He poked the items with the riding crop he carried.

'Bit full, isn't it?' the colonel asked. 'Enough equipment for two men. Why so, Private?'

'I am one of those designated to carry spares for the others, sir,' Murchison.

'Hmm. More neat than I expected from you, Private,' the colonel said with more than a trace of sarcasm. 'Close kit!'

'Yes, sir, thank you, sir,' Murchison said with a big grin.

The colonel had turned to go. He stood within a metre of Moody.

'Something amusing you, Private "AWL" Murchison?'

'No, sir. Just pleased to pass inspection, sir!'

'I'll bet you are!'

Murchison's action had distracted the colonel enough for him to hardly glance at Moody or Gill next to him. Soon he was ten paces away with the other officers. Horrie emitted a little growl of protest as two Arab boys on one rusty old bike circled the parade and were at their closest point to the dog. All the officers glanced back. Gill made a noise like a cross between a growl and a cough. One of the officers doubled back and confronted him.

'Throat problems, Private?' he asked.

'No, sir, I swallowed a fly, sir, I think.'

'You *think*? Wouldn't you know, Private?'

'There are other insects, sir!'

'Quite!' the officer said. 'Protein will do you good and won't kill you.' He eyed Gill before returning to the others. When the order was given to change to march formation, the Rebels all exchanged relieved glances. Command was then given to move off eight kilometres to the Ikingi Maryut rail station across the stony desert. It was going to be a hot, hard mission with full packs, some weighing 50 kilograms and including personal weapons, kitbags and sea kitbags.

Moody could feel Horrie moving. He was restless as the soldiers began to march across the desert, for he dearly wished to lead the battalion as he had on many occasions. Instead, he was a hot dog of despair, the only saving graces being that he was with Moody and moving at last. Moody kept whispering to him. Every time he spoke, Horrie moved a fraction. After about two kilometres, a truck driven by Ron Ford, the mechanic, came alongside the marchers.

'How's he doing?' Ford asked.

'Could you take him?' Moody asked. 'It's a bit hot for him.'

'No trouble.'

Moody broke ranks and hurried to the truck. He took the exhuberant Horrie out and handed him through the window to Ford.

'I have to deliver this load of equipment and weapons to the train. No idea what the next order will be so I'll tie him to that tree not far from the station.'

'The one that looks like it might be a gum tree?'

'That's the one.'

Horrie stuck his head out the window, tongue hanging out and panting. He whined and wanted to be back with Moody and the Rebels. Ford poured water into his food pan and Horrie lapped it up. Then Ford drove off, sparing the dog an arduous trek under a boiling sun. At the station, the thousand men milled around in groups, waiting for the order to embark. Moody slipped away out of sight and ran beyond the station to the solitary tree. Horrie was there, standing and looking towards the large group of soldiers. When he spotted Moody he jumped and twisted high, nearly throttling himself on the rope. Moody had no time to placate him. He bundled the little fellow back into the kitbag. Horrie stayed stock-still, perhaps thinking that his wriggling before had caused him to be separated from Moody and the Rebels. Moody hustled back to the station as the other began to move aboard. Once the train was moving, Moody removed him from the kitbag.

'Where's Fitzgerald's guard mob?' he asked.

'Other end of the train,' Murchison said. 'Anyway, Horrie'll be okay. That prick wouldn't turn him in with so many witnesses and mates.'

Horrie dashed around the carriage and to anyone who beckoned him. He brought smiles to the troops, who all patted him. The greetings done, he jumped to a window. Standing on his hind legs, he watched the passing parade of villages and country. No soldier was as intrigued or captivated by the sights as much as he was. He hardly turned his head away. Whenever he spotted an Arab he voiced his distaste, making the Rebels grin and discuss again what may have happened to him early in his life. He was agitated by Arab boys flogging food at stations, and when they laughed at his snarling, snapping face from the safety of the platform, he was beside himself with annoyance. A bold older Arab at one stop sidled to the Rebels' carriage and through an open window offered them whisky.

'Top Scottish! Top Scottish!' he told Murchison with a gap-toothed grin while stroking his grey beard and then glancing around to see if there were any military police watching. Murchison asked to see it and, satisfied with the label ('Glenfiddich single malt'), the sealed cork and its general look, bought it for 12 shillings. The Arab baulked away through the crowd as police spotted him. The train pulled out of the station. Murchison uncorked his purchase and found it was weak, warm tea. Brooker suggested that the only way it could have been dressed up so convincingly was to have poured the tea in through the bottom of the bottle. On close examination it was found that a small hole had been bored in the base. Once the real whisky was drained out and replaced with tea, the hole had been sealed up.

'You're lucky it wasn't camel's piss,' someone said with a laugh. Horrie took his eyes off the sweeping vista of rock and sand to examine the bottle. Murchison took his dish from Moody and poured the liquid into it. There was a roar of laughter as Horrie twitched his nose at the offering and backed away with an expression that said thanks but no thanks.

The train was pushed off to sidings on several occasions to allow other trains packed with troops to pass by. After several hours they reached Alexandria's outskirts just after noon.

'I'd like another night there one day,' Murchison said with a wistful gaze at the city, diverting the conversation from his duping by the old Arab to his cavorting with the two black prostitutes.

'In love, are we?' Brooker asked.

'You couldn't have coped, old man!' Murchison replied. 'But to answer your question, I did fancy one of them very much and I saw her several times. She was sweet and she liked me.'

'Oh, sure, and your wallet.'

'No. She didn't want money.'

'Oh, just a donation to the local mosque?'

'She was Christian. If you must know, I did give her something for her sick mother in Cairo.'

'And for her cat too, I hope.'

'We both gave donations to sick family members,' Fitzsimmons interjected, deadpan, and brought laughter that miffed Murchison, who acted as if his reputation for virility had been damaged.

Seeing his irritation, Brooker said: 'Don't worry, son, every woman in these parts has to provide for family members. You've done a great service to the community.'

At Alexandria's wharf, Moody beckoned to Horrie, who, looking resigned to his fate in the kitbag, hopped in without complaint. Moody gave him a last look and put his fingers to his lips, telling him to be very quiet. They lined up on the wharf with the others, who were in ranks of three. Their ship, the 3000 tonne *Chalka*, was in port waiting for them. It was pockmarked with shell and bomb hits from artillery and planes. The English crew was leaning on the rails and already passing the odd comment down to them.

'Any Don Bradmans amongst you Aussies?' one called and tossed an orange to the troops. When it was dropped, he added, 'Nar, didn't fink so!'

There was good-natured banter, and the crew looked pleased to be having them aboard. To the Rebels' relief there was not to be an inspection. Moody relaxed a fraction, and let Horrie poke his head out of the hole in the bag. Just as Moody's name was called, the dog was distracted by an Arab on the wharf. Moody raised his voice and shouted: 'Present, sir!'

Horrie growled. The officer glanced at Moody and his gaze lingered as he paused. It was a tense moment. Most officers didn't care about a few animals in the camps but with the prospect of combat they were frowned upon. Perhaps this officer was one of the few who turned a blind eye to such things. Maybe he didn't care, given that the men would soon be on a ship, where dogs and cats were tolerated depending on the captain and his crew. The *Chalka* had its own dog mascot, Ben, who much to the surprise of the Rebels was also an Egyptian terrier-cross. The Machine Gun Battalion very soon appreciated the friendliness of the English crew, who as they claimed ran 'a good and happy ship.'

Ben and Horrie were introduced and after several circles and examinations, decided they liked each other. A distinguishing factor was their tails. Ben had a proud, unclipped 'mast,' compared with Horrie's stump. Ben had been picked up in the recent battle for Benghazi between Commonwealth and Italian forces on the Libyan coast.

'Ben was left by the Eyeties,' a sailor explained, 'so he was one of the spoils of the victory and we couldn't resist the little blighter.'

Horrie was taken onto the deck in the afternoon. He was most unsure of what he was experiencing, with the moving deck and the blue and emerald water that undulated. Horrie stumbled to the railing and when he saw the drop, backed off. But his new 'best mate' Ben led him around the ship, helping him, it seemed, to acquire his sea legs. They even moved down steps to the ship's galley and the kitchen, where a delighted, podgy-faced Yorkshire cook found big bones for both of them. Horrie stumbled up the steps with his 'prize' but wished he hadn't when he reached the deck again. The boat began to roll and pitch. Horrie could not stand up and was at a loss over why. Every time he looked at the swells that appeared as if they might engulf the rugged, overcrowded boat, he shivered. The bone was forgotten. Moody noticed his distress and took him to their cabin, which provided little respite. Moody himself threw up and felt sick for the rest of the day and night. Day two was calmer and he spent three hours making a life-jacket for Horrie, but when he scampered off to play with Ben, he fought his way free of it. Moody had to keep a careful eye on him for the rest of the unpleasant journey.

7

PIRAEUS TO PAY

While the *Chalka* sailed on, the Germans attacked 19 Greek forts of the Metaxas Line in northern Greece, which resisted courageously but were overwhelmed by midday on 9 April 1941. This encouraged the Luftwaffe to attack the beautiful Athens port of Piraeus in the south, which was packed with shipping and the arrivals of British Commonwealth troops. German planes struck at dusk on the evening of the same day the *Chalka* steamed into Piraeus Harbour. Unaware of the coming Luftwaffe onslaught, it was an uplifting moment for all members of the battalion, after the bland rock and sand of Libya's barren Western Desert. Here at last was a vista that had been nourished by water with a vivid, dark green predominant in plants, particularly ferns with large fronds, and grass around neat, sloping rows of sandy-coloured villas and houses. The battalion disembarked and Moody lowered his kitbag, with Horrie in it, onto a small boat and into the arms of an unsuspecting, smiling Greek. He found he was holding a writhing ball of terrier. Before the local sailor toppled over, Moody relieved him of the kitbag and tried to placate Horrie, who was barking and growling. Moody soon realised why. The little boat was driven erratically as German planes swooped low from nowhere, bombing and strafing the new arrivals. The dog's antennae were working well, but were of little use now as the boat had to linger for several hours on the water during the persistent attacks. After the frustrating and nervous stay on the water, the boat darted its way to the shore. Once there, Moody let the dog free. He bounced around but was soon terrified as Greek anti-aircraft gunners opened up nearby. Moody grabbed Horrie and followed other Rebels towards the mouth of an open drain, where they ducked for cover. From that precarious vantage point 40 metres from the water, they watched as Luftwaffe planes careered down with a whine of engines and dropped bombs on the shipping, the big boats being the main target for sinking. As dusk fell, searchlights roamed the skies and German pilots flew daringly down the beam firing their machine guns. The darkening evening sky was now a fireworks show as tracer bullets, bombs and bursting shrapnel illuminated everything to the horizon.

Horrie was mortified and in complete capitulation to these conditions. He trembled and whimpered. Seeing his terror, Moody regretted bringing him. He did his best to soothe his fears, but all he could do was hold and stroke him and prevent him from running off. But when a bomb thumped hard close by and sent up a spray of rocks and dirt, Horrie's demeanour swung to the opposite extreme. He wriggled his way free from Moody and dashed into the open. He looked up at the planes and barked and barked, only taking a breath to growl before barking again. Having adjusted to the cacophony and ear-splitting noises, he was his defiant self, ready to take on the Luftwaffe. When the horror subsided, the battalion marched five kilometres to the little village of Daphni, erected tents and settled in for a few precious hours sleep, although the German attacks did not abate. Their bombs kept the ground shaking. The close hits sent dirt and stones spraying over the camp area. It showed that the Luftwaffe had managed to pinpoint the Machine Gunners' movements, which meant spies were passing coordinates and locations to the enemy. It told, without a word being spoken, that there would be no real respite or escape from attacks from now on if the weather held. This was the air arm of the mighty German war machine at its most menacing and deadly.

Horrie's bravery subsided in the night as he settled on Moody's bunk, looking to him for solace. Moody's responsibility to the pet meant he was disinclined to show fear so as not to trigger the dog's reaction, for like most animals, they sensed when humans were frightened. Moody was as on edge as the next Rebel, but his fatalism allowed him to adjust quicker than most to these dreadful conditions of real war. He took the attitude that he should not worry too much about events out of his and others' control. This sense seemed to transmit to Horrie, who gathered his wits against the new mind-numbing threat of bombs that left craters around them. Instead of barking at the 'eggs,' as the Rebels, to lessen their psychological impact a fraction, called them, Horrie growled every time one hit near to them. He remained shaken but not as much as when he was first on the shore.

*

Murchison was the first Rebel up in the morning, just before dawn on 10 April. The bombing had stopped two hours earlier at 4 a.m. and the other Rebels were snoring. Horrie heard movement, jumped from Moody's bunk and trotted out after Murchison, who stretched and looked to the horizon as light was beginning to distinguish the first glimpses of rural Greece. Murchison could make out sheep in a distant field with a shepherd herding them as if nothing had happened in the night. Despite the odd pockmark left by bombs, the fields were still green and inviting. In the paddock close by, the shapes of hanging grape vines were becoming visible, while the colour of poppies, red and purple, in the weak light, was brightening the entire area. Murchison encouraged Horrie to make his mark on the nearest tree, and then a second followed by a third and fourth. Just as he was marvelling at the little dog's bladder, he realised that the trees were gums, which could have been transported straight out of the Australian bush. Murchison felt good, despite a wary eye on the horizon, always half-expecting to see the Luftwaffe return, especially now that targets were visible. Then again, his worry was allayed in the knowledge that even German pilots suffered from fatigue, especially after hours of diving on Piraeus and its surrounds. And the visibility that would help the attackers would also aid the defenders with their anti-aircraft artillery. Any attacks in daylight would see Luftwaffe casualties increase.

One by one the Rebels came out of the tent and all made similar favourable noises when they saw the trees. Some followed Horrie's lead as they relieved themselves on a replica of a piece of home. Soon after dawn, scores of young Greek children wandered into the camp, but their attitude was at odds with that of the young Arabs. The Greeks looked upon the foreigners as heroes who had come to fight off the Germans and Italians. And Horrie, the barometer of all such invasions of the camps, only barked at them with approval as he weaved his way around them, played fetch-the-ball, and cheerfully greeted the smiling, inquisitive youngsters. This distinction continued to mystify the Rebels, who had disdained the Arabs' thieving, but still tolerated their cheeky commentary and bartering. The Rebels gave the Greek kids biscuits and bully beef, which were gratefully accepted. A tin was opened for Horrie but his gourmand's tastes, which had been honed by the cooks at Ikingi and on board ship, saw him screw up his nose and back away as if it was an insult to be offered the thick, chunky, dark brown coagulation. Horrie rushed off to find a cook but seemed miffed when he couldn't detect a tent harbouring one. Like the men, he would have to get used to the meagre fare that had sustained Anzac armies now in two world wars.

The men could see mighty Athens to the south. It had taken a bit of the overnight battering. But from their hill top at Daphni, it appeared to be its dignified, ancient and historic self, dominated by the ruins of the Acropolis, which had fallen victim to time rather than the Luftwaffe.

Mid-morning the camp was broken up and the battalion climbed into trucks for a winding drive to Athens. Moody took out his camera to capture as much as he could. He wished he was able to spend some time wandering this 3400-year-old city, one of the oldest in the world. He wrote in his diary that he intended to return, explore and learn as much about the place that held the home of Plato's Academy and Aristotle's Lyceum. Moody had studied the so-called cradle of Western civilisation and the birthplace of democracy. A poignant comment, perhaps reflecting his own fears, was a note that all this could be under threat very soon. The Germans, if they succeeded, would promise their own version of civilisation based on a military state, not democracy.

The threat from the invaders in the north was now palpable as the German 2nd Panzer Division captured the vital sea port of Thessaloniki, which had caused the Greek forces manning the forts on the Metaxas Line to surrender. The people of Athens turned out with emotion for the convoy, aware of the importance of help from foreign troops. Garlands and flowers were tossed their way from balconies; men and women in the street offered food. The cheering was inspiring as the Gunners responded, touched by the turnout and attitude. The battalion's departure from Sydney Harbour early in May 1940 had been spectacular when yachts, motorcraft and ferries had given them a wonderful send-off. But this Athens farewell was bigger, louder and more heartfelt. Australia had not then been in immediate danger. Greece was.

Horrie loved being the centre of attention. His barking and whirling tail from atop the Rebels' truck was all pleasure and he too seemed lifted. He kept jumping to face the well-wishers high above him and below in the street. Whistles had him almost spinning in delight as he tried to focus on the source. After his sea experience, keeping his feet on the top of the lumbering, bumping truck was easy. Horrie could not care why this moveable party was proceeding. He just responded to the smiles, clapping, pointing and yelling. His brain had long since sorted ridicule from love and liking and fun. And this experience was pure joy. Horrie looked to the Rebels, who applauded back to the Greeks and pointed out someone or something in the crowd. The trauma of the night was forgotten by the men and they were consumed by other emotions that were entangled with appreciation and motivation.

Murchison was not far behind Horrie in his enthusiasm, particularly for the myriad dark-haired, brown-eyed Greek women and girls. Most looked fetching in white blouses, and colourful blue and red vests, along with traditional neck-to-feet white dresses. Murchison was quick to respond to their open and closed hand greeting, which was wishing them luck and safe return from their mission. He blew kisses and pointed to taverns and cafes, indicating he would be back to see them all.

A chant went up from the crowd.

'What are they calling?' Murchison asked.

'I think it's "Benghazi,"' Moody replied.

'Don't they know the Germans have taken it back?'

None of the Rebels could explain the chant as it continued.

'They must know the 6th took it,' Gill said. 'Maybe they don't care that it has been recaptured. Perhaps our boys' reputation since then has been good . . . ?' The chant became louder. 'I dunno.'

'I reckon they just *want* us to be conquering heroes,' Fitzsimmons suggested. 'We represent hope that they will not be taken over by the Nazis.'

The convoy wound out of the city and headed north. Only a few high-level former footballers amidst the Gunners had been in front of such adoring, huge crowds. But for the rest, this was a first. Moody could only recall when he was cox for his house's winning crew at school. That was in front of a modest 300 people. This was a crowd a thousand times bigger. It took the Gunners an hour or two in the crawling trucks to settle their thoughts and to consider what lay ahead. They weaved their way inland and north: always north to the war. The Rebels were taken by the neat villages through which they passed. Moody took snaps of the churches in each little town with their tall steeples, and the white- or rustic-coloured villas.

Each place had people gathering around the village square and their ubiquitous white crosses, where the convoy was cheered each time. Cries of everything from 'Go in peace!' to 'Victory will be yours!' and 'God speed!' greeted them.

As they climbed through the country, they noticed that some women cried as they waved to them, which was a sobering sight for the battalion. Skullcapped, bearded men in long sheepskin coats and black trousers offered them bottles of homemade grappa and wine, which were accepted by the soldiers, as were some sharp knives of varying sizes. Horrie became the focus for all the locals, even more than he had been in Athens, as he pirouetted on the roof in response to the waving, blown kisses, laughing and cheering. Only once did he blot his copybook when, passing through a town 100 kilometres north-west of Athens, he barked so hard at something in the heavens that he fell on his back and rolled off the truck. His fall was broken by a black-frocked burly priest and another man, who passed the embarrassed and shaken dog back up to the Rebels. After much fussing about his wellbeing, Horrie continued his jumping about and barking, but with a fraction more caution than before. Just outside a village, Moody and Gill looked up to the source of the dog's continued excitement and spotted two planes of unknown origin and at a high enough altitude not to cause alarm. Their low rumble was heard as they flew in a wide circle as if noting the extent of the convoy. Then they disappeared.

'Luftwaffe,' Brooker said. 'Reconnaissance. We'll cop it sooner or later.'

8

THE PRACTICE RIDE

The battalion was close to the battle zone on the night of 10 April when they camped north of Larissa in green fields intermingled with red poppies in an idyllic setting similar to Daphni outside Athens. But there was no avoiding what the Rebels were about to face. They could hear the thunderous booms of the big guns and bombs; they could smell the cordite in intermittent wafts over the region; they could hear and see planes, still well overhead and not yet concerned with the Australian Machine Gunners. Early the next morning it was pouring rain and cold.

Brooker took Moody and Gill aside and told them: 'You two will go by bike today. Gillie, you are going south to pass a message to oncoming troops. Moods, you are to get a word to brigade's front HQ through the Thermopylae Pass.'

Both men felt tingles up their spine. They would be travelling alone and more than vulnerable if the Germans decided to attack from the air.

'Why have the Luftwaffe not come after us, do you think?' Gill asked.

'It's been pissing down. The clouds and storms may have made it difficult to achieve missions much beyond the front. Whatever it is, we are spared bombs for the moment. And it is very good luck for you two. When the weather clears they will come after our convoy first, and second, for fun they will come after you riding solo. They will come low and machine-gun you, maybe drop eggs too.'

Horrie sat watching Brooker as he spoke.

'What will you do with H?' he asked. 'Orders may see the lot of you split up very soon.'

'He must go with us,' Gill said. 'He is as important as any soldier.'

Moody reflected for a moment. He had to take responsibility. The Rebels as a group were most protective of Horrie. Each and every soldier enjoyed looking after him. Sometimes they even drew straws for the honour. But this was crunch time in his care. Moody was his master and while Horrie showed stump-wagging attention to all the men, he would go into a loving tail-spin when Moody returned from somewhere after they had been apart for even an hour. 'He'll come with me,' he said.

'On the bike?!' Brooker asked.

'Why not? If he can sit in a kitbag in the desert, he can lodge under my greatcoat.'

'Dangerous! I'm not sure I should let you take him.'

'Just as dangerous to leave him here.'

'Moods is right, Poppa,' Gill said. 'If he is going to be any use in the battle zone, he has to become familiar with everything.'

Brooker looked dubious.

'You saw him at Piraeus,' Moody added. 'He wet himself for about 15 minutes and then he was ready to take on the Luftwaffe—once he was used to the bombs and strafing.'

'All right,' Brooker said, 'you take him. But remember, don't take any silly risks to preserve the little digger. Look after number one first.'

'Don't worry,' Moody reassured him, 'it's my arse on the line. He'll just be there for the ride.'

*

Brooker furnished Moody with a map, which didn't give him much of an idea of the terrain he would be going through. Thermopylae Pass was on the east coast of central Greece, about 136 kilometres north-west of Athens. Some 2000 years ago the pass had once graced the coast but silting had widened the cliffs so that they were now 1.5 kilometres inland.

'Its name means "Hot Gates,"' Brooker told him, 'because it had and still has hot sulphur springs.'

'Got a new meaning now,' Moody said.

Ron Ford, who had driven a truck to the 6.5 kilometre pass and back, informed him that it was 'pretty narrow.'

Moody's guidebook, which he was referring to now much more than in the Western Desert, informed him that the pass had been the conduit for many invasions dating back to the second Persian hostile entry in August 480 BC. At that time, a small Greek force under the Spartan King Leonides defended Attica and Boeotia against the southward march of Xerxes' Persian army. Moody thought it a bad omen that the invaders had won that battle of Thermopylae and conquered central Greece. But he took solace from the fact that the Persians suffered huge losses in the conflict and that it had become synonymous through history with heroic resistance against the odds.

Moody put on his greatcoat, tying it at the waist with a thick belt, and took two practices to train Horrie to sit inside it. Horrie was content as long as he was close to his master, and his little cranium could poke out between a couple of buttons like a joey in a kangaroo pouch. Moody shook hands with all the other Rebels for, although nothing was said, farewells took on a greater poignancy now. They could not be sure if they would see each other again. Moody donned his goggles and black leather cap, strapped on his pack, revved his bike and was off, heading east on his mission. It was soon a sobering experience as he manoeuvred, skidded and shunted his way through the huge and growing throng of retreating Greek soldiers along with thousands of refugees fleeing the battle zone. Only Horrie's little face and his *yap, yap* greeting brought wan smiles on the road and in villages as Moody ploughed on through mud and slush. The rain continued to bucket down, adding minor flooding to the many travails of the fleeing masses. Yet every time Moody grumbled to himself about the conditions, he thought again of the blessing that the weather somehow had thwarted hammerings by the Luftwaffe, which had been seen in its full, relentless devilment at Piraeus when the skies were clear in the evening and into the night. The enemy efforts had destroyed it as a port. Moody rode in a climbing spiral until he reached the mountain top. He stood his bike. Horrie eased free and dashed around, lifting his leg here and there as Moody took in the magnificent vista of green fields dotted with farms, which stretched for miles below. In the distance to the north-east was the dominant Mount Olympus with its cap and necklaces of uneven white cloud. No wonder, Moody noted, that the ancient Greeks had believed that the gods lived there.

It was colder at this height and Moody noticed Horrie was shivering as he snuggled down in the greatcoat. On returning that night, Moody and Gill fashioned a body-stocking out of socks and slipped Horrie into it. At first, he tried to shake it off with a dance that amused them but he soon began to appreciate the warmth trapped around his little trunk. The two men thought of making booties for his four stumpy legs but as neither could knit, the idea was abandoned. So was a plan for a bonnet with a colour patch. Horrie just wouldn't wear it.

After that first 'mission'—really a practice run—of 12 April, the Rebels and the rest of the battalion were warned that the Luftwaffe would be at them within days. The weather forecast was good, which meant enemy planes could extricate themselves from runway mud and take off. Nothing could stop a German battering from the air with the Stukas, which were combined dive bomber and ground-attack aircraft. They were two-man planes with a pilot and rear gunner, which had first impacted on populations on the ground during the Spanish Civil War five years earlier. All the Machine Gun Battalion knew what to look for. The Stuka had inverted gull wings, fixed spanned undercarriage and its infamous 'Jericho trumpet' or wailing siren. It was the sound as much as anything that frightened its targets, but it was this that could alert any living thing with super-sensitive ears, such as Horrie. He picked up the ear-splitting sound anything up to 120 seconds before humans could see them, let alone hear them. The Stuka had some innovative designs, including pull-up dive brakes that ensured the aircraft recovered from its attack even if the pilot blacked out from the high acceleration. It was sturdy, accurate and very effective against ground targets such as long convoys the battalion would form, or even smaller ones such as motorcyclists.

There would be no British planes to take them on or do retaliatory bombing on German bases. The Germans had come to Greece determined to conquer the country mainly with the Stuka. This efficient dive bomber was taking the place of artillery. The Germans had stolen a march early on the Allies in World War I by putting all their betting chips on artillery. In this war they were ahead of the game again by relying on the Stukas, and the British and Anzacs had come unprepared for them. The Allies' advance air bases were small in number. Those in place had been blitzed and knocked out of action almost overnight. German Messerschmitt fighter aircraft hedge-hopped over the mountains, hitting one airfield after another and wiping out entire squadrons of British planes. Destructive waves of these German craft, and the Henkel, the first single-seater, turbojet fighter, never stopped. British crews often had no chance to jump in their Hurricane bombers, let alone load them. The Messerschmitt pilots were cunning and well organised tactically. They would fly high drawing ack-ack fire and then slice down beneath it to machine-gun the grounded and helpless British planes.

Many thought this overall masterstroke by the Germans would end the war before it got going. But in full British bulldog spirit, Britain's Prime Minister Churchill and his planners went through with the Greek campaign. Allied propaganda suggested that the Stukas were cumbersome and had to be escorted by fighter planes. This gave every gunner a sense they could fight back. The Australians were almost all gamblers and they liked the chance that they could 'win' at least a few encounters from the ground. The Stuka did have some vulnerabilities that had been passed on to all the 2/1 Battalion's gunners, and which had been exposed first in the Battle of Britain over British skies in the previous year, 1940. It had poor manoeuvrability; it was slow and lacked good defensive armament. The gunners were told that if they fixed their sights on one coming in, and if they could hold their nerve as it roared and whined at them, they had a chance of more than the odd 'kill.' Yet it was never easy for defenders on the ground. The ugly truth was that without a fight in the air and protection from British aircraft, the gunners on the ground were in for a torrid time.

Reports of breaking Greek resistance in the north-east were coming in. The battalion knew they would soon be attempting to counter the enemy in the air and on the ground, with German tanks leading the way in their prolonged 'blitzkrieg' operations. Brooker was giving orders with a new edge. There were fewer jokes and more repeated instructions as he split up the team for different operations. Featherstone, because of his stripe, would be first sent away to the front with the Gunners' A Company. He would be in charge of a section of attached signallers. Murchison volunteered to be a spotter on the adjutant's car, which meant he would ride on a sideboard and scan the skies with binoculars for the Stukas. He thought this might be an easier way to go, for the adjutant would be given privileges, as meagre as they were in the war zone.

The Rebels sat outside their tent smoking and cleaning their equipment as D Company marched off towards the conflict on the Albanian border. Minutes later, A, B and C Companies moved out to find two Australian and New Zealand brigades—a true Anzac force—who were having trouble holding positions just 25 kilometres north at Servia Pass. The Rebels called out words of encouragement but apart from that, said little to each other. There was tension in the group. Even Horrie was less exuberant as he picked up on the serious mood at the tent. He wandered among the group, looking for a pat, a smile or a word, and he received gentle focus, just enough to reinforce he was still wanted. His main attention was on Moody. Would he be sent somewhere and would Horrie go with him again? The thunder of oncoming and defending guns was closer now. Horrie pricked up his ears but was not alarmed enough to respond—not yet.

Brooker told Gill and Moody they would go on despatch-riding duties under the battalion's Corporal Thurgood.

'Well this is it,' Gill said, 'this is what we signed up for. Not quite the charge on Beersheba, but we'll be in the thick of it.'

'I dunno,' Moody replied with a wry grin. 'We'll be going a little quicker than the troopers and they didn't have anything like Stukas coming at them. And the tanks in the Great War weren't quite like the Panzers that blasted through Poland.'

The Stukas whistled by in the skies for the first time on 13 April and created a different atmosphere in the region and in the battalion's moveable base as it reached the foot of Mount Olympus where it would create its HQ. The gunners marched out to join the Anzacs, which had withdrawn already to a point about 15 kilometres north at what was called the Olympus–Aliakmon Line. The next day would be the beginning of the real war for Moody and Horrie.

9

DOG OF WAR

The morning of 14 April featured blues skies with just specks of fluffy cloud that would not hold back the Luftwaffe. Moody was up at dawn. He received orders to ride to the front with a message.

'Don't worry,' Brooker told him, trying to sound relaxed when he wasn't, 'it won't be your death warrant. The Stukas will have bigger targets to hit than you. You'd only be collateral damage, if you were very unlucky. There will be more problems with shelling. Just keep your head down and don't panic. You have an important job to do. Good luck to you and Horrie.'

Horrie heard his name mentioned. He looked up, his head cocked in enquiry.

'Yes, mate,' Moody said, 'you're coming with me. None of our mates will be in the camp until the afternoon. I'm not leaving you on your Pat [Malone].'

The dog waddled up and stood on his hind legs, his paws high on Moody's legs in reaction to the reassuring tone. Moody gathered his pack, put on his greatcoat and signalled to Horrie, who jumped up and nuzzled into position more eagerly than before. Moody adjusted his goggles, revved the bike and was away to the front. He began his trek up the road to Servia Pass and then the Alaikmon River where he was to deliver a despatch to the battalion's A Company Captain A. L. Vincent with the Anzac force.

Moody kept up a fair pace for a few kilometres but was soon retarded by thick mud, which he had to skid his way through here and there. He came across the result of the Luftwaffe's renewed efforts now that the Stukas could be extricated from their own mud impediments. The odd house between villages had been flattened and burnt out. Towns themselves had been partially destroyed. The shells of trucks, destroyed almost beyond recognition, littered the road and its sides. The stench of war—dominated by acrid smoke—became stronger as Moody gunned his machine, swerving to veer off the road in order to bypass oncoming cars, carts and trucks filled with fleeing refugees and their belongings. More telling than anything was the boom of the guns, which were coming nearer now as Moody could see the beginning of Servia Pass, which he had to negotiate to reach Captain Vincent. Moody glanced down at Horrie to see how he was coping with the scenes of misery. Despite the cold, his little head was out and his eyes darted this way and that, taking in every possible image as if it was a duty to note everything. He yapped at refugees, more in sympathy, especially for the odd dog or horse or cow, and his look lingered a fraction more on a dead animal lying by the road. It put Horrie in a sombre mood, which was very different from the one he had during the reception in Athens and towns now well south of them. Moody spoke the odd word of encouragement to the dog as his own heart beat faster the nearer they came to the hot spot. He was fearful of what lay ahead and if he would complete his mission, let alone make it back to HQ. Moody was beginning to be concerned too about the decision to take Horrie.

Then he noticed that the road ahead was deserted, giving him second thoughts about going on. Horrie was growling. The roar of his bike engine had drowned him out, and other noises had been submerged by the distant boom of artillery guns. Then he slowed his pace to about 50 kilometres an hour. Horrie was struggling to get out. Moody heard at first a low whine from somewhere. It became louder until it was a sound like 'a thousand screaming banshees.' Moody felt the hairs on his neck stand on end as a Stuka swooped and then dived perpendicularly. It spat bullets either side of his bike, causing mud to splatter up. Moody lost control of the machine for a second. It wobbled as he steered it off the road into a ditch of thick mud, which cushioned the crash and fall as Moody was thrown clear of the bike. He looked up to see the attacking craft climbing high in a long, lazy circle. Then he felt down into the coat for Horrie, who had not made a peep. Before he could assess the dog's condition, a second Stuka came zooming down with an ear-piercing blast that seemed louder than the first plane. There was nowhere to run now. Moody pressed down further into the mud as bullets pinged close. His attention turned once more to Horrie, worrying that his silence meant he had been hit and killed. Then a third German dive bomber careered from out of the sun much lower than the other two. It seemed to almost skim the road at him. The noise caused the terrified animal to demonstrate he was alive. He kicked and wriggled to get out of the coat. Moody tried to calm him. He looked up at the three planes as they circled now like huge buzzards taking their time to snare their weakened prey.

Moody was riveted by the devil's head insignia on the planes, which he could see clearly. He imagined the sadistic pleasure his masked tormenters were getting from the fear instilled into their would-be victims on the ground.

Moody's instinct was to get back on his bike and speed off. He righted the machine and blew hard with relief when it started first go. After an initial kick of panic, Horrie, apparently unhurt, was whimpering. Moody was just back on the bike when he heard a truck screech up close by. He jerked his head around and heard the most soothing words imaginable at that frightening moment: 'You all right, Dig?'

A bare-armed Australian driver, wearing a slouch hat and with a cigarette hanging from his mouth, looked down at him with a hint of concern. Moody assured him he was okay, as he explained that the planes had forced him off the road.

'Yeah, the ditch was handy for you,' the driver responded, his voice as calm as if Moody had just had a flat tyre rather than three Stukas doing their best to kill him. The driver enquired about his condition a second time and when Moody reassured him, the driver pointed ahead. Still with a languid, matter-of-fact tone, the driver advised him to race to Servia Pass, while warning that the Stukas would be back on him in a minute. Then the soldier drove off, crunching through the gears that would allow him to build some speed, but seemingly without being overly concerned. It was the inspiration Moody needed. He looked up to see those planes still circling, as their pilots and gunners appeared to be waiting for the best chance of a kill. Moody leaned over the handlebars and built to top speed. He passed the truck driver who had stopped for him and was soon weaving his way by another five vehicles, with 'spotters' on running boards scanning the skies. He was just ahead of them, still a few kilometres short of the pass—which was more a dip in a mountain than a constructed access—when the planes came hurtling at him with that now familiar and shattering high-pitched sound. Moody negotiated the cratered, slippery road and then slewed off it. He bounced away from the bike and dived for a ditch, holding Horrie so that he would not be squashed.

Moody looked up to see the Australian convoy of trucks halt and their occupants, some carrying rifles, run for the ditch and fields 50 metres from him. The planes let go bombs, which fell close, and fired their guns. Some of the soldiers lay on their backs and fired in defiance. Then the planes climbed high and away once more and the diggers rushed back to the trucks, started them up and were on their way. This happened twice more short of the pass as the German pilots seemed to enjoy this uneven cat-and-mouse 'game.' They hit one truck, disabled a second and wounded at least three men. At that rate, it seemed likely that the convoy might not even reach its destination with the loads of weapons, food and equipment. After the fourth attack, Horrie's courage returned. He was wriggling and barking. His stump of a tail was active. His ears were up, listening, concentrating, and waiting for the sound he would hear long before any human. Moody let him jump free. Horrie dashed along the road, sat, stood stock-still and then sat again. Then he bounced around barking at the sky. Moody waved at the convoy's lead truck and pointed at the dog and sky. He shouted warnings. Seeing this, the driver didn't wait for the word from the spotter on the truck. He called for everyone to dash for cover. This caused a chain reaction as all ten vehicles were abandoned. The planes careered in low. With plenty of warning, diggers lined up the planes and fired, causing one of the attackers to jerk about as if hit or trying to avoid enemy fire. Two bombs were dropped, causing Horrie to scamper for a furrow. The planes were one thing for him to 'manage.' He could hear them coming. He could see them roar overhead. But the sudden explosion of bombs was something he could not get his overactive mind around. There was no warning for him to pick up, no sound, and the falling devices were too fast and small for him to see. Yet still he growled, less certainly and without breaking into a defiant bark.

Moody stood and carried him to the bike as heads bobbed up in the fields beyond the road. Diggers began scurrying back to the trucks for another incremental crawl forward. They called defiant abuse at the planes. Some waved at Moody with a thumbs-up sign. Those in the front few trucks were well aware now that the small dog with the big bark was the best early-warning system. Moody patted Horrie.

'Might have saved a couple of dozen lives, my little mate,' he said, stroking him. 'Very good boy! Good fella!' Horrie tried to lick him. A few minutes later, there was a further attack from three Stukas and Horrie again was first to 'spot' them, his bark sending dozens of diggers running for cover. More bombs fell and he was disturbed a second time by the sound that he had no warning of. Moody was also frightened but somehow his responsibility for the dog helped steady his own nerves at critical moments. There were plenty more yells of thanks from the diggers as they rushed back to their trucks. They realised that Horrie's efforts were making the prime occupation of avoiding death less difficult.

Moody, followed by the convoy, reached the mouth of the pass, but the road itself now was an increased impediment to progress as potholes became bigger and bomb craters nearly covered the path. Each hole was filled with mud and slush, which made the bike ride a nightmare. Moody had to stop several times and walk the bike around the blocks. His staggered run now took him by the ancient town of Servia on Mount Olympus' western side. The classical architecture had been mostly destroyed and homes were burnt-out shells, some still smoking from recent bombs dropped by the Luftwaffe. To make appearances worse, Servia seemed to have been made a ghost town. Only a lonely dog, which received a sympathetic bark from Horrie, was visible. The inhabitants were now part of the exodus south.

On the road through the town, an Australian road patrolman on a motorbike warned him that German artillery was shelling Servia Pass. When he ascertained Moody had not made the run before, the patrolman pointed to the pass and told him to go hard for it. At its head, he was to wait for the flash of the guns. When he saw them he was to 'beat it through the bend before they fire the second shell.'

With the chilling experience of the combat zone backing his words, the patrolman added: 'Don't worry about the first shell. It will be at you as soon as you see the flash. If it has missed you, then go for your life.'

Moody was more nervous than ever before. *If it has missed me?* he thought. He could feel his heart pounding as it had in the mud ditch during the Stuka attacks. The patrolman asked if he was frightened. Moody assured him he wasn't when he couldn't recall being more so, and the discussion turned to the dog. Moments later, Moody, with Horrie tucked well down, was off at speed for the pass. He heard the sound of a plane above but it did not seem to be coming low and Horrie was not reacting to it. Pushing the bike hard, he reached the second bend as instructed and pulled up beside a stationary Australian truck. The driver had alighted. He was in the road watching the head of the pass.

'How you going, Dig?' Moody asked.

'Not bad, Dig,' the soldier said as he waited for the guns' flash as outlined by the patrolman, and then added more urgently, 'Here she comes!'

Moody followed him as the driver dashed for a ditch. An explosion followed, which he predicted would land artillery shells right on them. But it missed, instead landing hard on the embankment to their left. The driver reassured him there would a moment's respite now as he stood and brushed mud from his jacket. He warned that because the Germans were using a large mortar gun, they were capable of firing off a quick additional round of shells. Then the driver noticed Horrie. Moody took him out and the dog dashed about, making a tail-wagging fuss of both men.

'What a bonza little mate you have there!' the driver said, bending to pat Horrie. Frowning, the driver then suggested that he take Horrie until they were at the end of the pass. The road was broken up so badly, he added, that Moody would find it difficult to control the bike while dodging the enemy mortar fire. Moody agreed and handed Horrie to him. The driver took off with an anxious and perplexed Horrie watching through the window to see if his master would follow. Moody waved, jumped on his machine and made his run for the pass. He could not concern himself with the shells. It was nerve-racking enough just manoeuvring past all the craters and potholes on the badly damaged road, which was greasy with mud and oil. As shells whirred, spat and exploded around him, Moody leaned low over the handlebars, for psychological protection, if nothing else. The chances of being struck in the pass's confined space were higher than on the road. The showers of shells were whining in at him. Moody felt the hot 'whoosh' of the burning metal whistling close. The acrid smell in the pass was suffocating. The shells sprayed and bounced off the mountain's walls and there were no ditches or trenches in which to dive for cover. Moody had nothing on his mind but reaching the end of the pass, which he did after the most hair-raising ride of his life. As he slewed the bike to a stop, he had never felt more relieved. Even the fresh sounds of combat close by in the mountains were not as daunting.

Soon the truck rumbled up to him. Even before it braked and stopped, Horrie leapt from the window. After a cheery 'Good luck, Dig,' the driver was on his way. Moody reflected on how much he loved the loose and warm camaraderie of Australians at war, and how much of a leveller it was. He might never see the driver again or he might bump into him in some bar in Lebanon or Cairo, or

Sydney. But the man had done something in Moody's and Horrie's interests as a simple yet selfless gesture of support and humanity. Moody didn't wish war upon anybody but he acknowledged that it drew out the character of men: the best and the worst traits.

Moments after the truck was on its way down one path, Moody was into the hills to the west looking for and finding the battalion's B Company, where he reported to the Signals Unit. Once in the war zone, he became nervous about Horrie until the battalion's Signals' truck driver, Ron Baker, volunteered to take him back to HQ. Moody handed him over with further relief, knowing that there would be at least one or two Rebels to look after him by the time he returned. But about 20 minutes after giving up the saddened Horrie, Moody was ordered to carry a message to battalion HQ. He jumped on his bike and raced down to the pass in an attempt to overtake Baker and Horrie. This time he negotiated the pass more easily and with less concern, although the shelling had not stopped and the confined space and dark walls were still foreboding. Once past the depressing shell of the burnt-out Servia, Moody spotted Baker's truck.

Meanwhile Baker was alerted by Horrie sitting stock-still on the passenger seat, his head cocked and his ears trying to stay erect. He seemed to be trying to focus on another sound beyond the grumble of the truck engine. Baker was worried.

'What's up, mate?' Baker asked. Horrie ignored him.

'Gerry? Stukas? What?!'

Horrie began growling, then barking. He put his paws on the window, looked at the skies and kept up his warning. Baker pulled up the truck, grabbed Horrie and ran to the side of the road. Moody was about 150 metres behind them. He saw Baker, Horrie under his arm, diving for a ditch. Moody bumped and skidded off the road and ran for cover too. A squadron of Stukas made their now familiar dive, blaring, strafing and bombing. After three runs they climbed high and were gone.

Moody did not reach the truck until it was at HQ. Horrie was reunited with him, and they both visited the cook's kitchen for a well-earned meal.

Fitzsimmons spoke to Moody just before he had to leave camp in a truck on an assignment.

'I'd love to take Horrie, after what the drivers told me about his alerts at the pass,' he said as he bent down to fondle Horrie's ears, 'but I can see he is spent.'

'He'd go and do the job,' Moody said, 'but better to let him rest.'

'Yes, he's only human, after all.'

10

REBELS IN RETREAT

There was a reunion of the Rebels that night of 15 April minus Fitzsimmons and Harlor, who had been rushed to the front to replace two of the battalion's signallers, who had been killed. Everyone made a fuss of Horrie. His courage and intelligence at Servia Pass in adjusting to the terror of the Stukas, bombs and artillery had those who knew of his exploits saying that he was as important as any other individual in the Gunners because of his early-warning prowess. This assessment hastened the Rebels into working out a plan to make sure that whatever happened, he would not be abandoned. As a last resort, he would be given to the battalion doctor, Sholto Douglas, who was an admirer. His medical unit would be kept together more than any other. Moody had a word with the doctor, who was overworked and required for everything from extracting bullets and shrapnel to amputations and care for dying diggers. Douglas gave his word that he would take care of Horrie, should all the Rebels be incapacitated.

Despite it being spring, the weather was cold, sometimes freezing in the morning. Some of the hardier battalion members swam in a stream near their camp but often they would have to break through a thin layer of ice. Horrie was one of them, but his desire for a dip was questionable. The next morning he went for a dawn romp with Moody, Gill and Murchison and insisted on crossing a stream on a log ahead of the others. Halfway across he slipped and fell into the water, breaking the ice. He scrambled for the other side, much to the mirth of his 'walkers.' Then an incident occurred that they swore they would never forget, one of countless 'Horrieisms.' The dog had attempted to restore his dignity by beginning to cross the log from the other side. Halfway there again, he barked to get their attention and then fell into the water. All of them interpreted this as an attempt by the dog to show that his original 'slip' had been on purpose, which was really telling them that there was no need for them to laugh at him. It confirmed Moody's belief that the tiny animal had an enormous sense of dignity.

On returning to camp for breakfast, Horrie stopped. He sat like a stone statue. After a few seconds of monk-like contemplation of the skies, he growled. All heads turned to watch him.

'Uh-oh!' Murchison said. 'Horrie's at it!'

The three Rebels rushed to the tents and yelled for everyone to take cover. 'Planes! Gerry! Stukas!' were the cries as hundreds of men, half-naked or with only one boot on, ran towards trenches. Horrie was in an exhausting long-running bark. Gill counted more than a hundred continuous grunts from him before the Stukas were heard, swinging low out of the sun. Horrie himself led the Rebels in the dash for a trench. The Stukas did their worst, creating damage to vehicles that could not be hidden, and causing some cuts and bruises without any gunners being badly wounded, thanks to Horrie. When he emerged from the trench with Moody, Gill, Murchison, Featherstone and others, scores of men made their way to him to pat and thank him. As ever, the dog was chuffed at the attention. There was no doubt in any digger's mind that this amazing little quadruped knew what he was doing and without any signs of real anxiety, only impatience for his mates to follow him into the trenches.

There were no frivolous gestures towards him from the men. Many believed that they would have been killed by the attack as they lay in their beds in vulnerable tents and flimsy makeshift covers designed to keep out the bitter cold and winds, but not bombs and machine-gun bullets. His status as a battalion member, not just a pet or mascot, was confirmed. This was put to the test in the afternoon of 16 April when Horrie again alerted the entire camp. He led the way toward the trenches, his tail wagging as he looked back at the rushing Rebels all following his lead. But somehow in the mayhem, Moody and the other

Rebels lost sight of him. After the thundering, crashing, hellish Stuka attack, hundreds of battalion members emerged from their refuges. But not Horrie. Diggers came from all corners of the scattered camp to thank the little 'God Dog' as the padre preferred to call him (rather than 'Wog Dog'). But he was nowhere to be seen. A hundred gunners went out looking for him and when he couldn't be found, some feared the worst. The padre put up a prayer, but even that seemed to fall on deaf celestial ears until someone noticed a moving brown object in the latrine trench. It was Horrie covered in shit. He emerged with a happy face, and was confused by all the protests when he padded his way towards the Rebels. The rollicking ball of stench had everyone backing away in protest. Few of the grateful gunners were prepared to go near him and they called out their thanks from a distance. Moody assigned himself the thankless task of cleaning him up, and he used oil to do it. When a few of the gunners were reduced to expressions of mock anguish over the incident, Murchison blasted them, reminding all that he was not to be subject to derision or contemptuous laughter. Horrie *the War Dog* was placed above it all for the sake of his finely tuned feelings and sensitivities. But he still needed a very good wash.

*

Concerns increased for the battalion at the news that the hard-battling Greek allies, who were fighting for their homeland, were losing the fight on the Albanian flank and border with Italy. The force of the German army, the best equipped in the world, was beginning to tell on several fronts. The Rebels making the runs to the Anzac front were returning with pessimistic assessments. They reckoned they might be in for a fight to the death unless there was an exit plan and no one had heard of one. It was never discussed, at least not in the ranks, although officers poring over maps were beginning to face facts. They might have to think about a Gallipoli-like evacuation strategy. Greece was being overwhelmed by three encroaching enemy elements: their absolute superiority in the air; their Panzer tank divisions, which frightened and swept all before them, and without opposition from any equivalent armed vehicles; and their artillery power. These three military arms allowed the German soldiers and gunners to follow through and mop up. The Nazi military machine, fed on victory on several fronts in Europe and now the Mediterranean, was beginning to believe its own propaganda about invincibility. After a gallant, long hold-out, utterly spent and broken Greek soldiers began to straggle from the Albanian border in increased numbers among the never-ending flow of refugees. It was a sure sign that this war could only end in defeat for the Allies, who did not have the numbers or firepower to make a contest of the battles.

The gunners gave the Greek soldiers bully beef and any other food they could spare, along with warm clothes and blankets. The pitiful, desperate men were grateful; lost soldiers defeated in their own homeland. Only a few carried the type of rifle that was first seen 40 years earlier, and they were out of ammunition.

The Rebels all moved out at various times on 16 April to take despatches to fronts, which were getting harder to find. Defences were crumbling as the Germans pressed. Featherstone reached the battalion's A Company, which had just received instructions that they should keep going from Gerania, 30 kilometres west of Mount Olympus, and take up defensive positions between Tirnavos and Zarkos, towns 20 kilometres further south. The battalion's B Company was machine-gunned by Stukas at Servia Pass. A truck was destroyed and three men, including a signaller, Private H. D. Moran, were wounded. Moran died the next day (and was temporarily replaced by Brooker), but not before some measure of revenge had been secured by Lance Corporal Donald *Story* Gill from Geelong, Victoria (not to be confused with Moody's mate Donald *Munro* Gill from Signals). He manned his Bren gun at the pass for two days. A concerted Stuka attack attempted to wipe out the company's nearby HQ. D. S. Gill faced the onslaught and returned fire, bringing down two planes. Gill received the Military Cross for his brave efforts, but resistance like this was rare, such was the sheer weight of attacks from the air. Right along the front, the Anzacs began a slow withdrawal.

'We were ordered to support the withdrawal of our troops,' the battalion's Corporal W. J. Freeman noted. 'In doing so we caught sight of a German patrol about 1000 yards [900 metres] distant. We brought fire on them, causing them to take cover. We continued firing in that direction until the withdrawal was completed.'

In effect, the Germans could follow without losing great numbers of men and equipment as the Allies, caught in the refugee flight south, began a gradual pull-back.

The battalion's C Company was ordered to support a New Zealand brigade south of Servia. Murchison was to join C but, in the perpetual movement of troops, could not find it. He eventually discovered its gunners below the top of Servia Pass and to the left of the road that ran to the rubble that was once-pretty Servia. Murchison had to follow the trail of the gunners who had carried the always heavy load of weapons and ammunition on a rocky, narrow track across a steep gorge. He braved it alone, with just his trusty 'lethal weapon,' as he called his rifle, and the pistol that had once punched holes in the tent roof in the Western Desert. Two squads (32 men) of one platoon were spread 200 metres along the mountain. Murchison found his assignment sections perched where gunners loved to be: 20 metres above the pass with a good protection of rocks. They had built fair shelter under rocky outcrops, should the Stukas take a liking to them as targets. Yet despite their positioning the gunners were open to the skies. There would be shoot-outs with the Stukas' gunners. This was what they were in this battalion for: not easy kills of troops in trucks coming to the pass, although that was part of the job. The adrenalin rush came from taking on the enemy planes as they screamed down at them. The gunners on the ground turned their weapons up and held the *rat-tat-tat* at the enemy on the swoop in and swoop out in the hope that they would see a wobble, a spring of smoke or even flame before the long whining, spiralling death-dive.

Murchison was stunned by the sight of 30 Stukas droning in low, guns blazing and releasing bombs. It was a combined attack on the platoon's position as German infantry came at them from several angles with the aim of surrounding the Australian gunners. But somehow, inspired by their fearless Lieutenant R. G. Sampson (who would earn the Military Cross for this action), the gunners were able fend off, then capture 150 Germans, once the Stukas had drifted off to attempt damage elsewhere, or reload their bombs.

Murchison hoped he would survive the experience, just for the bragging rights back with the Rebels. He was able to use his rifle against the Stukas or their support planes. After only half a day with this platoon, he was ordered to take any vehicle he could manage a ride on across to two others about three kilometres to the left of the pass. These platoons were covering a river frontage of about six kilometres. Murchison found them with some difficulty after hitching rides with three trucks.

'Jesus,' he muttered to the 12 Platoon captain, as he tore his signals gear from his tired back, 'you must be bloody close to the front.' A few gunners grunted cynically at his awe.

'Mate,' the captain said, 'we are the bloody front-line.'

'There's no—' Murchison began.

'That's correct. There are no infantry in front of us.' He handed Murchison binoculars. 'See the river? That's the Aliakmon. Beyond that you can see a little town—Kazani. Note the road north of it. That's where Gerry will be marching to the river with nothing to stop them.'

'Range?' Murchison asked.

'About 3000 yards.'

Murchison handed back the binoculars in silence.

'We can't even place our guns in depth,' the captain said with a hand gesture indicating behind them. 'Gerry is coming in such numbers that we must be in one thin line of defence. We are doing what we can to give protection. That's all we can do.'

*

The true Anzacs among the diggers in the battalion, men such as Brooker, who had come all the way from Gallipoli in the last war, knew the signs. As he rode a motorcycle back to HQ, he had to pass the depressing sight of the road clogged now with trucks, vehicles, carts and refugees fleeing south, always south, squelching through an endless quagmire in the still-bitter cold winds and often sheeting rain. Brooker had most compassion for the old, young and the ill. Women with babies strapped to fronts and backs; old men in raggy jackets and threadbare trousers, with little children, some only barely able to walk, clinging to their uncle or grandfather. Brooker wanted to feed them all. He felt depressed about people who had dropped from exhaustion. Odds were, he reckoned, they would die. No one could afford to stop and help. But he did stop to hand his day's ration of bully beef to a woman who was stumbling and seemed likely to fall at any moment. She had a pusher holding two children, while one little boy straggled behind her crying and complaining. She blessed Brooker for his generosity, and then cried when he pulled from his pack a box of hard biscuits and handed that over too. She fell at his feet in gratitude. He was embarrassed, and he did not have the heart to tell her this food was no loss to him. Yet to her it was sustenance for her children. He made it clear with hand motions that she should break the biscuits up into little pieces and dunk them in water to soften them before she gave them to her children.

Brooker had been in the country less than a week and he already loved it and the people. He found the Greeks gracious and friendly. Even at this most grim of times, they maintained a quiet dignity. They were losing everything and he felt more than a twinge of guilt that for once his mighty Anzacs would not be able to defeat the enemy. His mind cast back to the Great War and how the diggers and troopers on the two major fronts had done more than any other armies to defeat the enemy and liberate the peoples of France and the Middle East by October 1918. There would be no repeats here. The sons of the vanquished had become the victors, and there was a measure of revenge in the goosestepping Nazi army. Instead of liberating towns in Greece, the battalion would now witness the opposite.

On 21 April 1941 the Greek government more than generously officially 'released' its Allied partners from the losing battle by advising them to withdraw their forces. It was clear to all diggers that this was the sentiment of the Greek population too.

'There were no reproaches from this wonderful people,' Cyril Falls wrote in the *Illustrated London News*, 'who bade our troops farewell with the kindliest of good wishes, and often urged them not to dally too long at the risk of capture. Where in history shall we find combined such tenacity of purpose [in the way the Greeks continue to fight in a losing cause], such purity of motives and such generous and gallant hearts?'

*

The Rebels linked up again and joined the listless, sad throng of people. Battalion members at least believed they would probably reach a troop ship, but there were no guarantees; no certainties. Stopping at a village north of Larissa, still about 400 kilometres by road to Athens, Moody noticed an old woman, dressed in black, struggling to dig a hole in which to place some precious tins of food. She would not have the strength to make the long journey on foot. Moody and Horrie wandered to her, and the dog looked questioningly at her efforts. His sad little face caused her to stop. She made some admiring noises and stopped to wipe her brow. Horrie, perhaps feeling the compassion of his master, waddled to her in supplication and licked her hands. The fierce little terrier, killer of poisonous snakes, nemesis of all people in Middle Eastern dress, attacker of all intruders into the Rebels' camp, and brave defender against hundreds of murderous planes, was now as sympathetic and soft as any creature could be. She pointed north and with gestures and a few words about the 'Devil' coming soon, made it clear she was doing this in preparation for the German takeover. Moody was touched. He completed the hole for her, dropped in her tins of food and covered them, so that the 'treasure' would not be discovered. While he toiled, the old woman had picked up Horrie and was sitting on a stone fence rocking him. The dog enjoyed her warmth and attention.

'I crossed over to her and taking Horrie put him within my coat,' Moody wrote. 'His little head popped out and gazed at the old woman. With tears welling in her eyes, she smiled and put one hand on mine and one on Horrie's head.'

Horrie licked her hand and Moody had to hold back tears himself as he bade her God's protection and hustled back to the slowly moving convoy that was being harassed by Stukas. Hundreds of Greeks joined the throng from the burnt-out shell of a town, Larissa. Only days earlier it had been a happy, if nervous village, whose inhabitants had turned out to cheer the foreign heroes who had come to defend Greece. The village was about 60 kilometres south of Servia Pass, which the Germans were already moving through despite strong resistance. The enemy had warned Larissa's inhabitants they had three hours to leave before they struck. Nuns in the town's convent were hustling out of the building about 40 little girls, aged from six to ten years and all dressed in white. They seemed unconcerned as six of them carried a sheet marked with a Red Cross, which was the universal sign that registered a hospital, or the wounded or injured, or those who were defenceless and not involved in the fighting. The sign was often painted on buildings in attempts to stop enemy forces bombing hospitals. The sheet that the girls were carrying would be seen easily from the air. The nuns would have thought this signature of neutrality would protect them. While others around them panicked and rushed to the local station where a train was waiting and already overcrowded, the children seemed happy not to run. They waved at the diggers. They were singing a happy little homage to Jesus. Moody and Gill were walking by and waved back. Horrie, perhaps stimulated by the sight of youngsters, wriggled inside Moody's coat and he was released for a 'pit stop' at a tree, before he bounded up to the girls and dashed around them. Even in the hurry and defiance of a nun's cry to 'keep moving,' a couple of the girls stopped to pat Horrie.

While people were still trying to climb aboard, the train began to kangaroo-hop out of the station before building to speed. Still some refugees struggled to climb on. Several fell off. Thousands of locals, including the girls from the convent, women and elderly, did not make it. They would be forced to move down the one, long exit road with the massing crowd of others, along with the escaping military convoy. The 1st Battalion Gunners would be called on to take up defensive positions if the enemy pressed too close or at strategic locations. A Company was ordered to the nearby Larissa airfield in case the Luftwaffe attempted to make it a base. Meanwhile, Stukas hovered overhead, a warning of threats to come. Then they struck. The Germans' warning to evacuate Larissa before it was destroyed from the air made it seem like a little touch of humanity had come from the Nazis. But this evaporated fast as the Stukas came down hard on the convoy. They were aiming at the trucks, but because they always missed more than they struck, there was 'collateral damage,' which often now meant human beings. The Rebels, without any signals assignments at this time, were asked to police the movement of traffic, with Corporal Thurgood, on his motorcycle, leading the Rebels in directing people and vehicles as if he were in outback Australia mustering sheep. It was a tough, thankless task as vehicles were hit and had to be bundled clear of the road to allow the seething mass of humanity to keep surging away from the attacking army. The Panzer division was being held up by Anzacs and others fighting a rearguard action. But the Germans were not acting with any great urgency on the ground. They thought the softening up by the Luftwaffe would make their task easier as the refugees surged on. Why overdo it and attack maniacally and deplete your force when you could not lose this 'contest'? The German commanders on the ground believed it was better to let the herd swell so it could be brutalised from the air.

The Stukas, in waves of 30 now, began their assaults. They did not have it all their own way as the battalion's companies moved off the road, set up their guns and blasted back. But the sheer weight of the air assaults meant it was an uneven fight.

Thurgood noticed that the battalion seemed to be one truck short. He rushed over to Moody and after a quick consultation, the two roared off on their bikes back to Larissa to see if the missing truck had broken down there, or if it had been destroyed. It was a dangerous manoeuvre for both men who reached top speed once past the rear of the refugees. They were racing right into the face of oncoming enemy, but there was a small window of opportunity to check the battered town before the German tanks rolled in. They wound their way through Larissa, which had been flattened. Hundreds of bodies were strewn in the streets. Thurgood and Moody could not find the missing truck and were just about to hurry off again when Thurgood skidded to a stop. About six of the little girls from the convent were sifting among the dozens of the bodies of their friends. Only one nun had survived. The bloodied and torn Red Cross flag-sheet was lying fluttering in the breeze. Thurgood pleaded with the nun to gather the few girls who had survived and to hasten to the refugees. They were too distraught to heed the advice.

A wave of mixed emotions swept over Moody as Thurgood shook his head and indicated they had to ride off. Horrie had poked his head out at the scene. After looking at it for several seconds and sniffing the stench of death in the air, he pulled his head in and shivered. Both men tried to convince at least one child each to ride pillion but the nuns would not allow what remained of the convent's group of pupils to be separated from the others.

'C'mon,' Thurgood said to Moody, pointing to an Australian ambulance truck that had rumbled up to the girls, 'the ambos will do what they can. There will be room in the ambulance, I would expect.'

Moody understood the chilling nuance of the remark. The mangled and dismembered bodies of the children and nuns indicated that all those hit were beyond help. They rode back to the convoy and went about their duties. But both men were affected more by the slaughter of the children than any other experience so far in the war. When night fell mercilessly and the convoy created a circular camp with trucks separated by 30 metres in case of a strike, Moody and Thurgood wanted to speak to someone about the convent girls at Larissa, but both wrote later that they could not bring themselves to do it. They feared they might burst into tears if they did.

After nightfall, Brooker discovered that two trucks must have taken a wrong turn before the camp, and they were missing. Gill had jumped on his Norton to find them and was also missing. Brooker and Thurgood organised drivers, including Ron Baker and Moody, in a little search party that retraced Gill's ride. They discovered the tyre marks of the trucks that had missed the turn-off. Brooker called off the search saying that Gill would find them before they were behind enemy lines, and guide them back to the battalion camp. As they reached the unit, Brooker spotted three fires high on a very steep hill about a hundred metres from the camp. The others were perplexed but their sergeant's experiences in the Great War caused him to exclaim: 'Bloody spies! Those fires will alert the Luftwaffe to our location!' He cursed and took an anti-tank gun from a truck. He marched 30 metres from the camp, set it up and fired in the direction of the fires.

'See who you've alerted now, you bloody bastards!' Brooker yelled in between bursts of the gun, which ruined the tranquil setting. It was effective. The fires went out.

'Good, you animals!' Brooker snarled as he put back the gun. 'You'd rather live than spy!'

He contemplated rounding up the probable fifth columnists. But all agreed that the gunners were exhausted. They guessed, more in hope than knowledge, that the spies in the hills would be well away after Brooker's crude exhibition of distaste for their activities.

Moody and the others went to bed, but his slumber was fitful as his mind worried over his 'lost' mates and the nightmare of the schoolgirls. He wandered through several emotions—fear, hate for the enemy, pity for the girls, pity for himself, worry about how this war would end for him, Horrie and his mates. Eventually fatigue from a rough day took over and he slumbered with vivid dreams and nightmares colliding.

11
FIREBUG

Brooker woke Moody at 2.30 a.m. It was his turn for sentry duty. He pulled on his boots and coat and wondered if he should bother to take Horrie or not. The little terrier seemed to be asleep under a blanket but when Moody reached for his rifle and revolver, Horrie bounced into his path.

'You want to go out in the cold?' Moody asked.

Horrie circled him, his tail wagging.

'Oh, you think it's a late-night walkie, do you?'

On hearing the W word, Horrie growled his approval and followed the half-awake Moody. They trundled up the hill that had harboured the fires six hours earlier and found the allotted sentry duty point. He settled in under a tree near some rocks with a view up the hill about

60 metres from the battalion camp. Horrie, wearing his own bodystocking coat, seemed pleased with his involvement with this strange assignment. He licked Moody and crunched on a bone salvaged from the cook. The faithful little friend was good company on a black, quiet night, which was only disturbed by the sound of distant artillery from the approaching enemy, perhaps 150 to 200 kilometres from them.

Like everyone else, Moody was on edge for this most unenvied soldierly duty. The night, the encroaching enemy, the shock of those fires on the hill and the stark recent memories of the slaughter at Larissa that had hardly left his conscious or unconscious mind, all crowded in on his thoughts. As the minutes ticked by he was more than grateful for Horrie's company. At just before 3 a.m. Horrie sat up from his lying position, where his head had rested on his paws. Those magnificent ears began to do their little dance as they focused on a shape *out there.* They tried to fix on something that was not quite right. Moody was snapped fully awake. Horrie growled. It was this throaty emission that had made him the hero of the battalion. He rarely wasted it and on most occasions it heralded unseen Stukas. But the little sentry was not gazing skyward. His eyes and ears were fixed further up the hill.

Horrie did not blink when Moody whispered to him. He was concentrating as hard as his exceptional faculties allowed him. Something out there had his undivided attention and this had readied Moody although he could not see or hear anything in the dark. His first thought was that it could be the 'spies' who had lit the fires earlier. Moody crouched close to Horrie, trying to sink low enough to be near the dog's eye-line. Horrie bristled. Moody knew something living had to be out there but it could be anything: a sheep, a wild cat, a stray dog . . . Moody put his hand on Horrie's back. He was shaking. The touch triggered the dog's movement forward a few metres. Moody knew his body language. Horrie was not in 'alert' stance. This was his predator mode. He growled with more force. Moody followed him. Horrie seemed intent on what appeared to be just another rock. Moody was nervous. He whispered for Horrie to 'stay' where he was and slipped around to outflank the object of Horrie's aggravation. But Horrie, as was his wont every now and again, did not obey his master. He rushed forward. The object took a human shape as a man stood. He wore traditional peasant's garb, including a sheepskin coat. He was young, Moody guessed in his early twenties. The man's hair was long. He spoke Greek and uttered friendly salutations. Yet, Moody wondered, what was he doing creeping so close to the gunners' camp in the dead of night? Moody aimed his rifle and called for the man to 'halt there.' He commanded Horrie to back off, which the dog did, reluctantly. Moody ordered the man down to the camp, with Horrie trotting along at his heel, growling with menace and itching to make a dash at the man's calf and ankle. Moody took him to the camp's commanding officer, Captain H. 'Syd' Plummer, 36, a short, trim officer with a gaze that never left the detainee. He mumbled, 'Well done,' to Moody, who gave full credit to Horrie, which caused a brief smile to wash over Plummer's serious expression. A Greek translator was summoned. Plummer questioned the peasant, whose manner flitted between extreme nervousness and attempts to be amiable. He claimed he was a local shepherd looking for lost sheep that often strayed over the hills at night. When questioned about the odd hours of his search, the peasant said he arose before dawn and often had to look for lost members of his flock. Plummer was calm in his interrogation, never raising his voice, but with enough pregnant pauses to make the detainee inclined to fill them.

'I was surprised at the trucks [in the camp],' the detainee said.

'Captain, he could not have seen the trucks from where he was found,' Moody interjected. Through the translator, Plummer challenged the man on this point. He seemed to fumble around, not giving a straight answer. It made Plummer suspicious. The detainee then blurted out that he had crouched down when he heard the dog growling. Again Moody disagreed. He suggested the man was already crouching before Horrie noticed him. The detainee said he had cowered and hidden when the dog came at him.

'I was scared I would be seen as a . . .' he began.

'A fifth columnist?' the translator asked in Greek.

The detainee answered, perhaps a little too quickly, that he agreed.

Apart from these unconvincing responses, there was no proof that he was other than that which he claimed.

Plummer spoke to a guard. 'Wait for an hour,' he said looking at his watch. 'It's nearly 4 a.m. . . . then escort him right out of the area.'

Moody searched the hill at dawn. There was no sign of any man or sheep in the area, or, he reckoned, any clue that anything had trodden on it recently. Moody informed the Rebels at breakfast of Horrie's further heroics. The dog received a round of sincere pats and cuddles of thanks that day from many battalion members once they heard about the events of the night. They believed that their mascot and honorary fellow member had saved them yet again.

*

The fifth columnists were growing in numbers as it became apparent that Greece would likely fall to the Germans. Most of them had been recruited by the ubiquitous Nazi secret police, the Gestapo, who used blackmail to gain assistance. The local agents were ordered to slow the Allied soldiers' retreat as much as possible. Apart from the damage being done to all towns by the Stukas, agents and spies were ordered to blow up buildings that would fall across the roads through villages and make the convoys' passage slower. The Allied truck movements were noted by spies and plans were made for locals to impede progress by pushing herds of cattle and sheep onto the road, or by laying concrete blocks. The truck drivers became irritated at having to stop and herd animals off the road, and soon they were ploughing right through them. But the more solid blocks had to be manually shoved or carried aside.

The Greeks villagers rushed forward to help despite the fact that the former Allied 'heroes' were being pushed south.

12
ROGUE ANZACS

Murchison found himself fighting a rearguard action on the front-line as the Germans advanced. He joined two Kiwis from the New Zealand brigade that had been fighting with the battalion's C Company. The three Anzacs linked with six Greeks who had drifted towards the action when their own army had disintegrated. Two of them had lost their boots and had replaced them with sacking bound around their feet. The leader of the little band of Greek fighters was Stavros, 30, a bearded, muscular, 183 cm former academic. His English was good. He explained to the Antipodeans: 'Why should we go home? Should we wait for the Nazis to come and destroy our villages and families? Just because our army is defeated, we, as individuals, are not. You are foreigners fighting our fight! We want to help you!'

Murchison and the Kiwis, Archie and Bash, were delighted at the Greek attitude and the nine rogue fighters together moved south of Servia Pass as night fell. They had one advantage over the oncoming enemy. They were a small enough group to be able to determine where the Germans, in their thousands, were situated. They could hear and see them. They could smell and see smoke from their camp fires and it was this that encouraged the group to make audacious moves. They had the element of surprise. But after dark, the surprise was for them when a German truck lumbered off the road in their direction. The group hid behind rocks, primed their rifles and watched. The Germans stopped at the foot of a mountain and proceeded to set up camp.

The little Allied team could hear the Germans shouting and laughing.

'Two officers and about ten men,' Stavros whispered to the others. 'They are a vanguard scout group.'

'It'd be good to get their truck,' Archie murmured. He was a nuggety fellow with a black beard that gave him a threatening look. Murchison had nicknamed him 'Ned'—after Ned Kelly.

The others mumbled their agreement.

'That means raiding them,' Murchison whispered. All were for it. Murchison organised that they surround the enemy camp and then charge in firing.

'No using taking them bloody prisoner,' Bash said. He was tall and angular, and also had a beard but with a reddish tinge.

'Okay,' Murchison whispered, 'I'll go for the officers. Knock 'em out first.'

He signalled with a dropping of a hand held high and led the charge into the camp, firing and yelling. His first shot hit an officer in the forehead and he slumped to his knees, killed instantly. The other officer reached for his Luger pistol but, before he could fire it, one of the Greeks slipped in from behind and ran a knife across his throat. Three other enemy soldiers fell the same way and the others bolted into the dark, with the Greeks firing and yelling after them. Stavros ordered them back. Murchison took one officer's cap and wore it. Stavros took another. Murchison removed the Luger from his victim's holster and jammed it in his belt. One of the Greeks grinned and handed him one of the Germans' knives. Murchison slid that into his belt too. He then went through the pockets of the dead officers and removed their gold wristwatches. Archie and Bash, both motor mechanics by trade, had the truck humming in a minute. The little Anzac–Greek band rumbled off down the road, passing a group of German soldiers marching in the same direction.

'Stay steady,' Murchison said, 'and hidden. They'll see our caps. They'll salute. They can't see us properly in the dark.'

As predicted, all the German soldiers gave rigid salutes. Murchison, with a quick, arrogant glance at them, saluted perfunctorily in response, just as he imagined a German officer would.

'Not like us,' Murchison laughed, 'so fucking disciplined!'

Stavros translated for his Greek men and they all gave understanding grins.

They rumbled along the potholed road.

'Reckon we're out of the enemy zone,' Bash remarked after half an hour. 'Better change trucks. Don't want any Anzacs to blow us apart.'

'Yeah,' Murchison agreed, 'but where from?'

'Don't worry about it, sport,' Arch said, 'Bash and I can get *anything* to work.'

They passed several burnt-out vehicles before Arch pointed to an Australian truck, which appeared in bad shape. Bullet holes pockmarked the sides and the roof had two big dents from bomb fragments. They stopped. Archie and Bash bustled straight into action. They hotwired the ignition. The engine coughed and died. This happened several times while the others surrounded the trucks, watching for any possible attackers. The two Kiwis slid under the truck and after some mechanics' talk, fiddled with the engine. Inside ten minutes they had the vehicle's engine purring. The rogue 'crew' jumped in, and they bumped off down the road, slipping into alarming road dips caused by bomb craters.

After another hour they were stopped at a roadblock by a small Anzac force.

'Halt!' an Australian voice called.

'Yeah sure, mate,' Murchison replied, 'we're all diggers.' And with a laugh added, 'Well, honorary ones, anyway.'

*

Don Gill had become lost searching for the battalion personnel in two missing trucks near Larissa. Travelling past the town, his bike had broken down after he had been driven off the road in a Stuka attack. He was close to a truck that had also taken evasive action sending up a wall of dust. It was just the sign that Stukas and single German Henkel bombers looked for. Minutes after the first attack, one such lone Henkel could be seen wheeling around at low altitude in the distance. Gill was about to find better cover when he saw six of his battalion gunners jump from the truck with their weapons. The sergeant among them called: 'Aircraft! Action! Fire!'

The Henkel came swooping so low that it looked as if it might land. The gunners fired and caused the pilot to be distracted enough for him to jerk the controls. The plane's bullets whistled over the gunners and into a swampy field beyond the road. The Henkel pilot pulled out of his skimming ride and climbed away. Gill yelled to the gunners.

'Can you shoot?' the sergeant called back.

'Yes!' Gill replied. He was ordered to grab a weapon from the truck and line up next to them, which he did. The Henkel came in again as Gill, cool as ever, assembled the weapon. He was looking through the sights as the German plane swung low at them. All the gunners opened up too early this time, except for Gill, who was not quite ready. He aimed just as the Henkel dropped two bombs, one which slid over the other side of a mound, and another that seemed right on them. But it did not explode; instead it clunked hard onto the ground about 20 metres clear of them, dead centre in the road. Gill kept firing as the Henkel roared away. The plane seemed to tilt a fraction, then a thin trail of smoke spiralled from it, causing it to lose altitude over the hills on the horizon. The gunners did not wait to hear the crash or see if smoke billowed up. Gill joined them as they all dashed for the truck, aware that the unexploded bomb could detonate. When they were a few hundred metres away, the sergeant offered Gill a smoke. 'I think you got yourself a "kill," cobber,' he said, low-key. 'Congratulations.'

One by one the gunners shook his hand without much more than a grunt and a brief grin.

'Bit of a lucky strike,' Gill said, matter-of-factly. 'Haven't fired one since practice at Salisbury Plain.'

The sergeant shook his head, dragged on his cigarette, smiled and said: 'It's never lucky when you hit 'em, Dig, never.'

Like Murchison, Gill had little choice but to stay with this splinter group. But he was happy to do so. Seeing the calm manner in which they had set themselves up ready for combat, he knew they would have a chance of reaching south to the battalion base, with a slice of luck.

*

Later Gill's group stopped for a further smoke and feed off the main road and down a dirt track to an olive grove close to a creek. They came across a group of eight Greeks who looked dispirited and bedraggled. Their leader explained they had not eaten for two days. The gunners offered them food and drink, which the Greeks readily accepted. After a half-hour, Gill and the gunners decided to have a wash in the creek. They were all filthy and had not had this chance at luxury for days. Finding soap in the truck, the Australians stripped and entered the creek, spreading along it about 30 metres. The Greeks remained smoking and eating, which was their luxury moment too. A few minutes later a squadron of Stukas came floating by high above from a southerly direction, indicating they had probably dropped all their bombs for that particular run. But when they saw the band of Allies, they decided to change course and strafe them, hoping for an extra bonus kill or two at the end of a day's work. The Australians called for the Greeks to take cover, and did so themselves, jamming close to rocks in the creek. But the fatigued Greeks seemed to have a careless attitude. They sat where they were and continued to eat and smoke. The Stukas hit in a one-off run and bullets spat and kicked up dust right through the camp. Three Greeks were hit. The Australians dashed out of the creek to help. One Greek had been killed and the other two were injured. The gunners, who all knew first aid, dressed the wounds. But within 20 minutes a second Greek died. The little Allied party buried the two men and took off in the truck with the third victim, who had been hit in the arm and shoulder.

When asked later why they had not tried to find cover, one of the Greeks said that they'd had so many narrow escapes that they thought their chances of being hit were the same whatever they did. It was a little too fatalistic for the pragmatic gunners but they understood the reason for the attitude, and the odds.

*

The next morning, 24 April, Murchison's band of Allies drove to a Greek inn in the village of Ulanda, which was the home town of a couple of the team. The innkeeper and several other locals were regaled with the story of the previous night's escapade. Wine, beer and whisky were soon being consumed. Murchison broke into a song about his battalion's division (the 6th) and 'Old Blamey's Boys.' He was off-key but wine had oiled his tonsils enough for a stirring rendition, which boomed out into the street. He climbed onto a table. The Greeks and Kiwis surrounded the table and tried to sing along, with Stavros explaining a few of the lines he could comprehend, which included a chorus of: 'Old Blamey's boys, 6th Divvy boys, Fighting for victory, liberty, democracy . . . !'

They were in full cacophonous flight when Brooker and Moody walked in. Murchison jumped from the table just as Horrie, his behind in a permanent whirl of joy, struggled from Moody's coat to greet Murchison, who picked him up and held him high.

'Horrie!' he yelled to the rogue group. 'This is the most important member of my battalion! He is our angel dropped into the desert to become our watchdog! Saved every one of us at some time or another!'

The Greeks crowded in to make a fuss of Horrie, who couldn't get enough of it. Murchison told them of the dog's exploits. Horrie began licking Murchison's dirt-smeared face and blood on his tunic. Moody noticed it and asked if it was his.

'No, mate,' Murchison said, removing his German officer's cap, 'the claret belongs to a very dead enemy officer.' He handed Moody the cap. 'As does this . . .' and tapped the Luger, 'and this . . .' indicating the knife in his belt.

Murchison told the tale of their night. As he did so, Horrie wandered outside and along the street, looking for a butcher's shop. He passed an overcoated man of about 35, wearing a black beret and sitting on a bench, sketching buildings in the street. Horrie stopped to sniff a parcel on the bench. The man muttered and lashed out with his boot. It caught Horrie a glancing blow on the side. The dog yelped and jumped back, more in fright than hurt, just as Moody came out of the inn looking for him.

'Hey!' Moody called. 'Don't you touch that dog!'

He hurried up to the man and remonstrated with him. The man pretended not to understand and went on sketching. Moody was in two minds about reprisals, but after a quick examination of Horrie, whose pride had been hurt and nothing else, decided against it. He picked up

Horrie and was walking back to the inn when a middle-aged Greek woman approached him. She kept pointing at the man on the bench saying under her breath: *'Kataskopos! Kataskopos!'*

Moody brought her into the inn, where she spoke to the Greeks. It was soon ascertained that the man was not from their village. He had been sitting and sketching for several hours. The woman said he was more interested in the military moving through the village, especially the trucks' markings, than drawing the quaint shopfronts. Three of the Greeks from Murchison's rogue group slung their rifles over their shoulders and hurried out. Murchison, Moody and Brooker followed. When the man noticed the group marching his way, he jumped from the bench, grabbed his parcel and ran out of the village.

The Greeks broke into a run after him. One fired his rifle above the man's head. When a second bullet whistled closer, the man stopped and raised his hands, one of which still clutched a sheaf of papers; the other held the parcel. Murchison was angry. He wanted to deal with the man.

'If he's a bloody spy, we should execute him!' he yelled.

Brooker and Moody restrained him.

'Let them handle it,' Moody said. 'It's their village and he's Greek.'

'Yeah, and take that bloody cap off before someone puts a bullet in you by mistake!' Brooker said. It was a sobering thought for Murchison, who pocketed the cap.

The Australians, with Horrie back in Moody's coat but with his head poking out inquisitively, watched as the

Greeks examined the papers that the interloper was reluctant to hand over. They discarded the artwork and became animated over the other hidden sheets. The Greeks abused and spat on the man. They marched him about 30 metres into some woods. Less than a minute later, two shots rang out. After administering their rough justice, the Greeks returned and showed the Australians about 20 sheets. Each carried notes on all the Allied vehicles, personnel and other military details. The parcel had two pieces of equipment hidden under meat that had attracted Horrie. The signallers recognised parts of a radio transmitter.

Murchison led them all back to the inn. He took one of the watches he had rifled from the German officers, placed it on the counter as payment and ordered drinks for everyone. Brooker pocketed the watch, telling Murchison he would regret selling it. More Greek soldiers wandered in and the party continued. But some home truths were revealed. Murchison was adamant that the Anzacs would have to evacuate. He spoke of what he had just been through and how fragmented the Allied and Greek armies were now, just marauding groups like his little rogue force. In his euphoric state he reckoned that the Greeks could be organised into a resistance movement in the hills.

'And how long would that last?' Brooker asked. 'The Germans would overwhelm us easily. They have the numbers. They've got a dominant air force and tanks.'

'Yeah, well,' Murchison replied, 'so if we got tired of fighting we could commandeer fishing boats for a chug-chug across the deep blue Mediterranean to Egypt, couldn't we?'

They were soon drowned out by the roar of applause for the news that Turkey had declared war on Germany. Greeks jumped on tables and chairs and began singing. The party atmosphere increased and the alcohol flowed. Soon the patrons were overflowing into the street. There was wild talk about what Turkey's intervention could mean. Further speculation fuelled rumours that the British might rush more troops and more equipment to Greece for a counterattack.

'Why would Churchill bother about the "underbelly of Europe" now?' Moody asked as they went outside to be heard, 'when the Germans have effectively won Greece and he has more than enough on his hands in Western Europe?'

'Exactly,' Brooker said, 'we are finished here. It's going to be a backs-to-the-wall fight all the way.'

Just when they were contemplating the immediate future, Horrie began barking. He darted towards a lean figure so covered in mud and grime that he was almost unrecognisable until his distinctive throaty voice greeted them with 'G'day, Rebels!'

It was Gill, who was embraced by a relieved Moody. Horrie did a little jig. Gill's arrival with news that Featherstone, Fitzsimmons and Harlor had been found and were back at camp called for another round of celebratory drinks. Brooker was overjoyed that his little band of Rebels was back together, almost, and intact. And there was a further positive feeling that during the day many of the 6th Division's combat troops had reached the area. There were plenty of soldiers left in what now seemed a lost cause.

'You know what day it is tomorrow?' Brooker asked. 'It's Anzac Day—25 April. A good omen that the Rebels are united again . . .'

13

NIGHT RIDERS

Intelligence reached Brooker that the Germans were planning to drop a force of paratroopers about 160 kilometres south of them at Corinth. Their main objective would be to blow up the canal bridge there, which would cut off the long divisional convoy in its attempt to reach the south for a possible evacuation from the ports—but not from Piraeus, which had been ruined by the Luftwaffe. As soon as darkness began to fall, the trucks were assembled. Brooker allowed the Kiwis and Greeks who had been with Murchison to join the battalion. The Greeks piled into the battered truck at the end of the convoy that had brought them to Ulanda. Despite appearances, it was running well enough. Archie and Bash offered to travel with them, but the Greeks insisted they could handle the crowded vehicle, which was also stacked with supplies, as were most of the others.

The 200-truck convoy moved off under the cover of darkness but the rush caused them to flick on their lights to avoid crashes or slipping off the road. Moody's bike had broken down after weeks of hard riding in rough conditions. This led to him and Horrie and some of the Rebels travelling with Ron Baker in his truck. The dog enjoyed the freedom of not being in the greatcoat, although he never complained. It was warm and safe and he was disciplined in the cramped conditions. But now he could take up any position he liked, his favourite seat being the front where he kept a vigil on the passing parade and villages, even in the poor light. Often he would give a little whimper, having seen something that human eyes could not: perhaps a knot of people, a few sheep, a stray cow or a cat. Only twice did he do a tremulous complete circle in the seat. Ron Baker next to him assumed he had spotted dogs.

They reached Corinth at about 4.30 a.m. A cheer went up from the front trucks when they reached the canal bridge. It was intact. The German paratroopers had not made their sabotage drop and it was assumed they would fall from the sky at dawn to make their mission less dangerous and more accurate. The convoy thundered on in one continuous snake down through the mountain levels to Argos. The road train pulled into olive groves where the trucks were given crude camouflage. The soldiers began digging trenches for protection from the expected Luftwaffe sallies. It was soon discovered that the truckload of

Greeks from Murchison's rogue group was not with them. It was surmised that their vehicle must have broken down somewhere en route. They would be isolated and caught up in enemy territory and this was confirmed when word reached the signallers that hundreds of enemy paratroopers had dropped in on the villagers in Corinth. They had rushed to lay charges on the canal bridge, which they blew up, apparently without realising that the main convoy had beaten them through by less than an hour. This sabotage was now self-harm. The German advance would later be held up by their engineers having to reconstruct the crossing. It was a rare blunder in German planning, always so precise, especially when there was no opposition to their manoeuvres.

This intelligence meant that the battalion and other 6th Division troops could relax for an hour or two knowing that the only major threat for the moment could be from the air. The Rebels and Horrie wandered into Argos to see if they could find a cafe that would sell them food and alcohol. Moody brought his camera and his ubiquitous travel book, and reminded the others that Argos had been a substantial agrarian village for 7000 years.

Reading from the travel book, Moody informed them that Argos once rivalled Sparta in its military strength and importance as a trade centre. Fitzsimmons took the book from Moody and after running his finger down the page, remarked: 'Listen to this boys: "Argos is the birthplace of the mythological character Perseus." I find that is very satisfying to know.'

That brought a few laughs. They found a cafe, which was just opening, and they sat down outside. Horrie dashed across the road to a small cottage and harassed a hen and her chickens.

'Little bugger must be hungry,' Moody said, and snapped an order for him stop his antics. Horrie trotted over, looking back at the hen. The cafe manager sold them wine but had no food. After sitting there for 20 minutes they were about to leave when an old woman in black wandered from the cottage across the road and offered them two trussed-up chickens. She had noticed Horrie's enthusiasm for the hen and guessed that the Rebels might be hungry. The lads insisted on paying her, and she seemed insulted. Then she invited them to join her in her vine-covered cottage. They accepted and followed her inside the modest home, cluttered with pictures, icons and several little crosses on the walls. She bustled about and brought out plenty of olives, cheese, bread and milk and made them tea. They felt more than a tinge of guilt when she showed them photos of her husband and son, who had been fighting the Italians in Albania. With hand movements and welling eyes, she explained that they had both been killed in action. Brooker tried not to show emotion, but he and all the Rebels were touched. She was alone with just memories. They expressed their helplessness to each other as they left the sad scene.

'We're bloody impotent!' Harlor exclaimed. 'These people are so generous and friendly and we can't lift a finger to help them!'

'We would if we could,' Brooker said, 'but we can't, okay? We must leave this beautiful country if we can. That's it. Those are the orders!'

They had a nervous day to contemplate their fates before the last convoy run at night to the coastal town of Kalamata, about 100 kilometres south-west. They roasted the two chickens that the old woman had prepared for them, and enjoyed the break from bully beef and biscuits. Horrie was thrown the bones and he feasted on what he could claim was his idea in the first place.

'We have to reward that lovely woman,' Moody said. The Rebels then gathered spare stores including food, clothing and blankets, bundled them together and left it on her front-door step with a note.

The overcast weather may well have prevented a Luftwaffe attack, but it was also thought that the enemy believed that the division's convoy was still hidden somewhere north of Corinth and south of Lamia. Whatever the reason, Anzac Day 1941 was a fortunate 24 hours at a critical time for the division. The good luck continued well into the evening and night as the convoy started its final run at 9 p.m. and moved at a more leisurely pace with less fear about air attacks. They arrived at Kalamata on the Ionian Sea coast at 2.15 a.m. where the battalion found many other Australian, British, and New Zealand troops, along with Greek and Yugoslav soldier contingents, who were keen to avoid becoming German POWs. Trucks kept pouring in and officers did their best to organise defences, the destruction of as much equipment as possible and the orderly preparation for boarding ships. The main targets for obliteration were the trucks. Soldiers such as Archie and Bash, who had spent their working lives saving and resuscitating vehicles, now had to put those skills into seizing engines. It was a sad business for them and all the other mechanics and drivers who had cared for their vehicles with such diligence. Others were assigned to ram shells the wrong way down artillery gun barrels and fire the charges.

'It's just like the Light Horse troopers in the Middle East in the last war,' Brooker observed. 'They were ordered to turn their horses in and they shot them themselves and it caused great pain for all the men, who'd gotten real close to their horses.'

'I've got news for you, Poppa,' Murchison said, 'we have to shoot 'em here too.'

Brooker grimaced in disgust.

'Well they won't be shooting any dogs,' Moody said with a glance in Horrie's direction.

'Oh, we all agree with that,' Murchison said. 'I reckon there would be mutiny if Horrie was threatened that way.'

Archie led the way with the Rebels in the destruction of vehicles. He started the engine and put a heavy rock on the accelerator. Then he slid on his back under the truck and used a spanner to remove the drain plug in the sump. When the oil drained away, the racing engine began to scream. Horrie was alerted, at first perhaps thinking he had somehow missed the whine of the Stukas, but his ears adjusted. Now he barked in protest as the engine noise reached an intolerable pitch. He ran away and only returned when the white hot motor, oil-less and without life, seized, bringing a sudden silence.

That done, Archie apologised to Horrie and began shooting holes in tyres or slicing them open.

'Used to do this as a kid in Wellington,' Archie said with disgust as he slashed another tyre. He put a bullet in another.

'Yeah, but then it was for fun,' Bash said, while draining water from an engine, 'now it's for survival.'

The two Kiwis became tired of draining the engines. They were soon seen smashing them with crowbars. And when they became fatigued with that, they ran the engines, drove the vehicles to the edge of cliffs and sent them crashing into forest below.

Instead of getting rid of food and bedding, the Rebels commandeered a truck, filled it with those goods and drove it into the village where it was distributed among the grateful townsfolk, who were worried about what the coming Nazi occupation could mean. In another part of town, a battalion officer, John Bellair, jumped in his truck and shot the lock off a chest that had come everywhere with him. It contained a smart tailor-made uniform that 6th Division had advised all officers to purchase in readiness for the 'triumphal march through Athens after we have thrown the Germans out of Greece.' Bellair reckoned he wouldn't be needing it now, so he gave it to an old peasant who worked in the surrounding olive groves. His beautiful tie was handed over to a 'skinny nine-year-old boy who used it as a belt to keep up his ragged pants.'

At dawn, the Luftwaffe began their runs over the countryside, strafing and bombing, causing the thousands of Allied soldiers to take cover but with no concern for their trucks now. The Stukas did their worst but were up against a stronger defence than elsewhere as hundreds of anti-aircraft weapons were lined up in a rough semicircle on the outskirts of Kalamata. This made it less difficult for the British Sunderland flying boats to swoop in, land on water and take off with a load of the wounded for transferring to ships. Some combined intelligence work by British spies stationed near German air bases at Larissa and other aerodromes alerted the pilots of the four-engine Sunderlands on the timing for their dashes to Kalamata.

Moody and Gill edged close to the beach and allowed Horrie to dash around on his twice-daily exercise, which was fitted in between Luftwaffe attacks. They watched as four Sunderlands wobbled in for perfect landings on a flat, calm sea. Boats carrying up to 100 wounded soldiers were ferried to the planes. The men were stretchered and eased on board, 25 on each Sunderland. The flying boats' two pilots, engineer and two bowmen all hustled to settle the wounded in. Anchors were barely dropped before being hauled in.

Horrie caused all heads to turn as he bounced around and then barked out to sea, wagging his tail. But this was not his 'warning' about Stukas. He was simply voicing his approval or amazement as the flying boats' engines roared and they clipped along the water's edge, hovered for about 40 metres and then eased skywards, aiming to reach British ships. Yet Horrie spent much time doing what he had gained fame for, by barking at the sky as the Stukas attacked six times during the day, which was hell for the weary troops. Locals helped conceal them all around the village and port and in the hills. But the Germans knew they were there in big numbers and they were doing their best to slaughter them. The older Greeks were stoic and few asked to be taken from their villages, but younger people, especially the women, pleaded with the foreign soldiers to allow them to escape. This created more heart-wrenching moments for all the Rebels.

Fitzsimmons wrote to his family: 'I spoke to two lovely 18-year-old girls, who offered everything, and I mean *everything*, they had for us to stow them away. They held my arm; they begged, they cried . . . We all would have liked to have taken hundreds of the Greeks of all ages but it was impossible. Some of us swore we'd return to liberate them. But this was cold comfort for those who wanted to leave right then . . .'

Moody came to the aid of the girls by finding Australian slouch hats and uniforms for them, and suggesting they stow away with the battalion. The girls toiled with the men in creating barricades, clearing roads and filling in potholes and bomb craters. Moody and Fitzsimmons believed they could be smuggled out on their boat in the dark and rush to leave.

Thousands of soldiers were assembled on the beach before midnight. The Rebels, and their two Kiwi recruits Archie and Bash, were close together. The stowaway girls, head down and quiet, were nearby. Moody had given away his greatcoat. There was nowhere to hide Horrie but it didn't matter. There was no inspection in this hurried evacuation; there would be no trouble in getting him on board. The dog remained calm and quiet, now experienced at sea ventures and 'leaving' or moving out from anywhere. He was content if Moody and the Rebels were close. They waited in silence for a sign of the rescue ships. At 1.30 a.m. a low ripple of appreciation and relief filtered along the crowded beach as lights could be seen on the water in the distance. Rescue was at hand.

14

COSTA RICA CALAMITY

A flotilla of small craft meandered into the Kalamata wharves and beaches and then ferried the evacuees to troop ships further out to sea. The escape was orderly although the troops were not lined up. Their selflessness and discipline, either drummed into them militarily or otherwise, saw the big assembly ease forward as the seamen manoeuvred their boats efficiently from the beach to the destroyers and back until not one digger remained. The gunners' battalion was placed on the *Defender* and slipped to the troop ship *Costa Rica*, a chartered Dutch ship. Everyone was given a chunky corned beef sandwich garnished with relish, and a cup of hot chocolate as a 'welcome on board.' It was a gesture appreciated by all who just tolerated their usual food. Horrie received his sandwich and when he wolfed it down and looked up appealingly to the Dutchmen handing them out, he received a second, much to the approval of all in view. More than 3000 soldiers from the battalion and other 6th Division contingents were on board.

As dawn broke, several troop ships were steaming away from the Greek coast with the *Costa Rica* on the left flank, the *City of London* in the centre and the *Delawarra* on the right flank. The *Costa Rica*'s escort was comprised of three destroyers—*Defender*, *Hareward* and *Hero*—along with the cruiser *Calcutta.* Everyone braced themselves for an attack from the Luftwaffe. Soon after first light, Horrie was on deck with Moody and Gill, and all heads turned to him as he became unsettled. He sat; he stood; he sat again. Then those now-famous ears began to straighten and face beyond the sea to the north. The cry went up that Stukas were on the way. Even before his first growl, gunners were moving fast to set up their Bren guns. Gill lined up with them and countless others. He readied his rifle. This caused Moody to carry Horrie to the sun deck and tie him up, much to his disapproval, as the Stukas began to whine their way towards the vulnerable troop ships. Moody grabbed his own weapon and, lining up next to Gill, began firing at the planes. Soon hundreds of men were crouched on deck, firing machine guns, rifles and revolvers. This was more than a useful back-up for the anti-aircraft guns on the destroyers. The Luftwaffe, which had long ago defeated any British fighters, for once would not have a battle all its own way. The chances of them being shot down increased a few percentage points, a situation that caused German pilots little moments of hesitation in their attacks. They were not suicide bombers and they had not had such concentrated, strong retaliation before in the Battle of Greece. The planes jerked and zigzagged in. This caused bombs to be dumped with a muffled explosion or none at all as they missed the boats and hit the water. One brave or foolhardy pilot dipped low over the *Costa Rica*, aiming his guns and bombs at the *City of London.* Some bullets of the deafening volley from the *Costa Rica* deck hit their mark. The Stuka stuttered in the air, coughed and then nosedived into the sea. A huge roar erupted from the two ships. Soldiers on the *City of London* acknowledged the hit with waves and cheering to the 1st Battalion gunners and the hundreds of riflemen.

Moody glanced at Horrie, who was barking another warning, and then up to see the 'gamest man' on the ship. He was perched in the crow's nest on the tallest mast. He was waving his arms like a demented conductor as he noticed another wave of Stukas climbing down from the sun. Bullets caused chips to fly off the mast and to fray its rigging.

Moody was in awe of the bravery of the man in the swaying crow's nest as he seemed to be right in the centre of the cross-fire coming down from the planes and up from the ship's deck.

When the squadron had departed, a bizarre scene developed in the saloon where one of the gunners, who could not secure a weapon, began belting out a tune on the piano. Other soldiers without guns gathered around and could be heard singing. This prompted Horrie to lift his head and bark and howl, which he always did when the men turned to song. His lyrical accompaniment caused the entire deck of gunners to roar with laugher. But then he stopped mid-song. He sat. His ears began to dance and quiver. Warnings were called along the deck. The gunners and riflemen were soon preoccupied with another Luftwaffe attack. All weapons aimed high. Another Stuka was hit and went twisting and shrieking hard into the sea, where it broke up. The deck of gunners cheered as one. Horrie had watched the incident and he barked as the Mediterranean devoured the broken bits of the plane, and the pilot who was never seen. The dog's apparent approval brought cheers and clapping from the gunners, whose adrenalin was flowing. Yet the euphoria was short-lived. The German pilots, twice bitten by the battalion's gunners, now shied away from the *Costa Rica* and concentrated on the not-so-well protected *City of London.* But enough defence ripped back at the planes for them to fly high and away to lick wounds and reload with more bombs and bullets. The third, fourth and fifth Stuka attack waves each lost a plane. By midday, the count was five down.

The *City of London* sent a signal to the *Costa Rica* congratulating them on the weight of their small-arms fire in support of the gunners, and encouraging them to keep it up as spare ammunition was passed around the deck, ready for the next inevitable encounter. Using the blinding sun as a backdrop better as it reached the peak of its arc, the

Luftwaffe returned. One bomb came close and rocked the boat. Some men were knocked off their feet as a tsunami-like wave swamped the deck, brought down rigging and stopped the boat's engines. The captain was informed that the ship had been holed. The engine room was engulfed in water. The engines were moved off their mounting and the ship ground to a halt. A silence enveloped the ship. The destroyer *Defender* cruised alongside and enquired about the problem with a loudhailer. Several wags called out responses: 'Just taking a breather!'; 'Forgot the batteries!'; 'Run out of petrol!'; 'Run out of coal!' The officer with the hailer called that his boat would start taking troops off the *Costa Rica.* Moody dashed for the sun deck to rescue Horrie, but the boat was slanting to starboard already. This ship was going belly up from what at first seemed a minor 'bump' from a bomb. He reached Horrie, who was struggling to keep his feet but as soon as Moody appeared he wagged his tail as if this was just another odd event on the sea to which he had to adjust. Moody was on edge as men began leaping down on ropes to the destroyer. He looked up, concerned that a new sweep of Stukas would return for a big 'kill' now that thousands of soldiers were in danger. Moody held Horrie and looked down to the destroyer, which disappeared out of view with the rise and fall of the water's swell. There was a seven metre drop. Moody had a small backpack. He would need two hands free to slide down a rope. There was only one thing to do. He would have to throw his little mate overboard. He called down to deckhands on the destroyer that Horrie was coming.

He held him up. Two deckhands grinned and gave him the thumbs-up. Moody waited until the boat's rise was at its lowest and then heaved Horrie, who did something akin to a double somersault with pike right into the two pairs of sturdy hands. Once righted, he looked stunned for a second, then wagged his tail and licked his catchers. Horrie's first afterthought was to look up for his master, who waved, relieved, before leaping for a rope and landing close to the dog, who went into a licking frenzy as if it was a game. Moody looked around for a good place to tie him up and decided on one of the destroyer's lifeboats. Moody then hurried back to help other soldiers as they dropped in by rope. There was a never-ending cascade of them hitting the decks and he broke the fall of man after man. But it was a dangerous operation. Moody saw one man drop too high in the sway between the boats. He hit the side of the destroyer and was thrown into the sea. The man did not surface and disappeared under the destroyer. Moments later another soldier tried to make the leap without using a rope when the boats were at their closest. But his timing was out. He hit both boats, struck the water hard and also did not surface. Small boats moved in and around but could not find the two men. With others falling into the water, the rescue flotilla had no choice but to help those they could reach.

Moody noticed a lifeboat slipping down from the *Costa Rica* and heading for the lifeboat harbouring Horrie. Moody dashed across the deck, untied Horrie and leapt clear a second before the lifeboat cannoned into the one on the destroyer. Moody looked back to see the two boats splintered in half by the impact.

'A close call, Horrie, mate!' Moody mumbled. 'A very close call!'

Seconds later Moody witnessed another incident that would stay with him for life. Bill McMillan, a quartermaster sergeant with the battalion's C Company, ducked when hit by what he thought was a piece of debris. But it was his *cat*, the half-Persian Ooboo, who had jumped ship. The cat clung to his shoulders. McMillan grabbed Ooboo and kissed him.

'You little darling!' McMillan said, steadying himself in the bobbing little boat. 'I looked for you everywhere! How many lives is that you have left?!' He gave the watching Moody the thumbs-up. Ooboo, like Horrie, was known to most in the battalion. Similar to Horrie, he was a mascot and had travelled as such with C Company through Egypt and Greece. But the cat had had a different route into the battalion. Ooboo had survived the evacuation of Allied troops from Dunkirk in 1940 and had been given to the gunners by a British contingent as a gift.

Moody tied Horrie to a pole centre-deck and returned to help others coming in. It was precarious. More men slipped and fell into the water. They had to be fished out of the sea in a frantic yet this time successful bid to get almost everyone on the destroyer and another that manoeuvred to help take passengers. Murchison, Gill and Brooker had stayed on board the doomed and listing *Costa Rica* with the last group of men, all officers, including the short, rotund captain. The three had combined with Moody to guide and help hundreds of men on the leap from boat to boat. The captain approached the Rebels and others with his most vital papers and some boxes tucked under his arm. He struggled to maintain his feet on his now acutely sloping ship. But he had the presence of mind, and eccentricity, to hand the boxes—containing long Uppmann cigars—to the Rebels and others who had stayed to near the end. All except the captain made the leap to safety. He was left standing on the deck and looked as if he might go down with the ship. The Rebels and a hundred other soldiers and sailors urged him to jump. He appeared torn, but at the last moment grabbed a rope, papers still under one arm, and swung out over the destroyer as its engines started up. Horrie craned his neck to see the captain hovering high over him. Then the skipper dropped, and without losing his feet landed centre-deck a metre or so from the dog. Horrie wagged his behind as if applauding his effort and final decision, and the captain made a special fuss of him as if what he'd just done was all in a day's work. But everyone knew it was tragic for the captain to lose his serviceable and hardy old tub. He had been with it 17 years and a decade of this was as captain.

All boats headed off for Suda Bay, Crete, the elongated, mountainous Greek island, 272 kilometres long by 32 kilometres wide. The soldiers were thankful that the Luftwaffe, again for reasons only known to it, had held off during the turmoil of a sinking ship. Otherwise there would have been carnage. The escapees had gone just four kilometres when all looked back at the *Costa Rica.* Its bow went straight up. Then it slid down stern first into the flat sea that had lost its turbulence now that the destroyers were well away. Everyone stared. No one said a word. The captain watched and crossed himself, perhaps wondering if he should have carried on the questionable naval tradition of going down with the ship. Horrie appeared so engrossed in the ship's dramatic yet graceful demise that Moody took his camera from his backpack and stole a picture of his beloved pet. It did not distract the dog one iota, and Moody wondered what he could be thinking. Horrie's concentrated expression flitted between confusion and sadness. But Moody, too, was distressed. All his wonderful photographs, diaries, keepsakes and other personal items, such as letters received on the trip, were now deep with the fishes of the Mediterranean. The loss of the diaries hurt him. He had documented the entire trip in them with diligence and in his smooth, stylish handwriting. He vowed to himself there and then he would attempt to re-create the notes, which were so important to him. But the loss of the artistic photographs upset him most. They could not be re-created; not unless he returned to the locations—a thin ray of consolation and hope for the future. Later shots could not match the originals: of Gill and the other Rebels at the Pyramids, in the bazaars of Cairo or in the many quaint towns and villages of Greece; or on Salisbury Plain in England. Some of the gunners had other more prosaic yet more practical thoughts and misgivings about their Vickers machine guns hitting the ocean bottom, too, and being unsalvageable. To men at war, those weapons were precious. Like the mechanics with their trucks, the guns had been lovingly cared for each day with cleaning, oiling and dismembering for inspection, along with their tripods. This valuable equipment, their raison d'être and the lifeblood of the gunners' battalion, had been lugged up mountains, across rivers and along countless kilometres of dusty, rotten road. With them, these diggers believed they were as near to invincible as soldiers could be. Without them, they were not so sure. The *Costa Rica*'s sinking left them disgruntled and wondering where they would obtain anything like the weapons they'd had.

15

A CRETAN AFFAIR

The Luftwaffe planes, loaded up with bombs, greeted the battalion at Crete with the same demonic gusto they had when the troops had landed in Greece. But this time the destroyers were able to at least respond to the Stukas' attacks, and make them less effective. Moody, Gill and the other Rebels were disappointed not to have their rifles, which had allowed them at least token resistance. Instead, they were left with a dash up the beach at Glaros, a few kilometres west of Chania on the north coast. Horrie led the way with leaps and barks. They found cover where they could in rough, half-dug trenches and cuttings. When the German planes had finished and flown off, Brooker led some of the Rebels inland for a 'transit' depot near the town of Chania. They moved through olive groves, barley fields and vines on hills. No spare metre was wasted; the Cretans had created giant 'steps' up the hills and mountains in order to cultivate more crop areas. The men passed tranquil little farmhouses and were enchanted by Crete. Above them loomed the mountains. The Rebels, the two stowaway girls and hundreds of bedraggled diggers, many survivors from sunken vessels, converged on the depot, which was well prepared. The soldiers were all given a cup of tea and food. Most flopped in nearby olive groves, ate and rested in the shade. Soon the Rebels were reunited, much to the delight of Horrie, who was the centre of attention as usual. They were visited by a battalion gunner, Les Jeffers, who told them he had saved Horrie. Moody was perplexed, knowing that Horrie was somewhere in the grove fossicking around as always in a new territory. But out of curiosity he accompanied Jeffers to another part of the field. From a distance, the dog he was about to meet was like Horrie, but on closer inspection there were a few distinguishing features. For a start, it was female. Her ears were floppier; she had a longer tail and the expression was different. Jeffers had noticed her at the Kalamata beach, and, believing she was Horrie, had taken her on board the escape boats. He had protected her when the *Costa Rica* went down. Jeffers was disappointed that he had taken someone's dog by mistake but Moody consoled him by saying that Jeffers had saved her and he should be proud of that. Her owner may have been killed in the air attacks. There was no knowing her history but, Moody pointed out, he had given her a future. Moody volunteered to take the female, whom he christened 'Horrietta.' He introduced her to Horrie, who was more than pleased to make her acquaintance.

'Must be a breed of them,' Fitzsimmons remarked as the Rebels watched the 'dance' of introduction. 'There was Ben on the Pommie merchant ship, who could have been Horrie's brother. Now this one could be his sister. And a couple of us saw the type in the Cairo bazaars.'

'They're a breed all right,' Brooker commented, 'a Gypo terrier. And what a fine breed. Intelligent, resilient, loyal and yet good watchdogs.'

'Not Horrietta, I'm afraid,' Moody said, 'Les Jeffers reckons she's incredibly timid. She didn't handle the Stukas at all well.'

'No one does!' Brooker said.

'We must look after her,' Moody said with a shake of his head, 'but the next few weeks may not be fun if Gerry hits hard.'

'Oh, our Nazi friends will come after us for sure,' Brooker said. 'Gordie has already picked up German intelligence comments about an airborne attack of paratroopers.'

'Nice, when we haven't got all our weapons!' Murchison said.

'Which reminds me,' Brooker remarked with a snap of his fingers, 'all our rifles are to be commandeered for combat troops. You can keep your revolvers and knives but the rifles have to go.'

Moments later, Horrie began growling and barking at the sky. Less than a minute later, a wave of German bombers scorched the skies and strafed the area, causing the Rebels to scramble for any cover they could find. Horrietta froze in terror. Horrie bounced around her and all but nudged her in the direction of a foxhole, into which she eventually cowered.

'What was wrong with Horrie's hearing?' Murchison asked as several lay protected in a large water pipe. 'They were on us much quicker than normal after his warning.'

'How's yours when you are concentrating on a lovely young woman for the first time?' Moody asked. 'Don't worry; once they are firmer friends he'll be as alert as ever.'

*

The two dogs became good companions and both led the details by walking out in front of the platoon when it was detailed to dig trenches, prepare fortifications and other chores in readiness for the Luftwaffe and what might follow. Then the air strikes intensified in the softening-up process that preceded the German tactic of paratrooper raids. Horrietta could not cope, despite Horrie's admirable entreaties to follow him into the foxhole. She froze, trembling and unable even to whimper. Horrie managed to coax her down the foxhole on occasions but sometimes it was impossible, which led to one or other of the Rebels dashing out from cover and carrying her shaking little body to safe ground. The men were concerned and Brooker said they would have to put her down. He suggested drawing straws to decide who would shoot her. The Rebels all had some rural experience, which included the killing of disabled animals. But none relished the job, especially as she had been such a pleasant addition to the Rebels and for Horrie, when the bombs weren't crashing around her.

Harlor suggested they find a local farm family to take Horrietta, which everyone agreed was a sensible solution, especially as none of them wished to play executioner. In the meantime, between Stuka attacks, she became enchanted with Horrie, the brave one, who knew how to handle every situation, especially in finding food. But she had one trick that he could not manage, which was to beg by sitting back on her tail, with her paws held limply in front of her. Moody was challenged to teach it to Horrie but he refused, saying it was demeaning to the animal.

Horrie often strayed from the camp but always returned at meal time. One night he did not turn up. All the Rebels searched in vain for him around their camp area. Moody was concerned. The next morning they would have to move to another part of the island and there was a chance Horrie would be left behind. The Rebels and other sections of the 1st Battalion did not have weapons and therefore would not be needed for the coming German invasion. They expected to be evacuated before serious hostilities. The Rebels were packing up at dawn when Horrie came whirring into the camp, more thrilled than anyone had ever seen him before. His behind gyrated so much that he moved in swirling circles in and around the delighted group. Moody examined a rope that had been tied to his collar. Horrie had chewed through it. Perhaps some well-meaning digger or local had found him running around. They may have believed he was lost and had tied him up.

'Had a chain been used,' Moody noted, 'Horrie would have been left behind.'

The Rebels moved camp closer to Suda Bay and that morning the Luftwaffe menaced shipping in a continuous, intense bomb barrage. It was too much for the terrified Horrietta, who vomited in fear. This was enough for Brooker, who ordered that she be taken inland to a local family. Murchison created a diversion for Horrie by taking him on a romp through the fields and along a donkey track. Moody and Gill then went in the other direction, where Harlor had the day before come across a family nestled in a valley well clear of Suda Bay and insulated to a comfortable degree from the sound of exploding bombs on the coast. The Cretan family—a couple and three children—were delighted to accept Horrietta. Moody and Gill stayed for some coffee and with limited communication were more than satisfied that Horrietta would be well treated. They returned to camp before Murchison and Horrie. The latter bounded about in search of his little companion but, when he couldn't find her, did not appear to be disturbed by her absence.

'It was a useful time to separate them,' Harlor wrote in a letter to friend in Australia. 'They only knew each other a few days, and not long enough to be pining for each other. Besides, we could only really attempt to get away with carrying around one dog with us, and that has to be in secret. That one choice would forever be Horrie.'

The Rebels' new camp overlooked Suda Bay. Below were several locations of British and Anzac troops on rocky hills. They were there to defend against any sudden arrival of airborne German paratroopers. More intelligence reports picked up by the Rebels' radio tranceivers revealed they were doing intensive air-drop training on Greece's coastline. The Allies were expecting the biggest ever assault of this kind. There was a nervous wait for all defenders, and communications were vital. The Rebels' job in part was to keep messages flowing between the scattered troops and HQ, located at the bottom of the hills and not far from the beach. In daylight hours they used a white shirt attached to a stick to signal Morse code. At night there was a problem. Any flashing by night of torches or lamps would be easily spotted by local spies, and even those out to sea already doing fifth-columnist work for the ubiquitous and efficient Gestapo. Urgent messages were coming through to the signallers more frequently now, and these had to be transmitted to HQ at ground level. The hills were too steep or rocky for men to negotiate. Brooker held a meeting to decide what to do. Horrie sat down and listened to the chatter as he often did, turning his head to each Rebel as if he was following the conversation.

'Horrie's our man,' Moody said. 'All you have to do is to tie a message to his collar and tell him to run to me. I'll camp at the base of the hill near HQ.'

'Nah,' Murchison objected, 'I can make it down the hill faster than Horrie.'

'Not at night, mate,' Gill said.

'Any time!' Murchison retorted.

Some of the Rebels agreed with him. Fitzsimmons suggested that Horrie was more likely to be injured hurtling down the hill at night than Murchison.

'One way to settle this,' Brooker said, 'we'll have a race in daylight. Horrie versus Murchie. The winner gets to be the runner.'

Bets were laid by many of the battalion on the outcome for the following day. Moody gave Horrie one training run in the early afternoon. He and Gill took him down the hill to Moody's camping spot near a hollow olive tree 20 metres from HQ. Then Gill returned to the main Rebels camp halfway up the hill and sent Horrie down again with a message directing him to 'take it to Moods, there's a good dog!' Horrie leapt off like a hare and took the note attached to his collar straight to his master. Moody made a fuss of his effort. That was enough training for him. A few hours later, hundreds of gunners and diggers turned out at points along the steep route down to HQ.

Murchison and Horrie took their positions at the starting position in the Rebels' camp. Gill squatted next to Horrie and pointed down the hill, where Horrie had been with Moody a few hours earlier. He attached a message secured inside a handkerchief to his collar, saying: 'That's a good boy, Horrie. You take the message to Moods, all right?'

The dog looked animated at this game. He glanced up at Murchison who remarked in a tone of mock indignation: 'Hey! That's cheating! He should not get coaching like that!'

The battalion group gathered around was amused. Fitzsimmons said in cheeky voice: 'That's a good fella, Murchie. Take the message to Moods. Go on! You can do it!'

The onlookers roared laughing. Brooker fired his pistol and they were off. At first Horrie seemed to think he should be running with Murchison and he kept pace, but with onlookers urging him on, he soon bolted downhill, dodging branches, leaping down from rock to rock, and skipping in a rush along the meagre path. He was soon 10, 20 and 30 metres in front. Murchison hurried his climb down but lurched forward, his fall only broken by a fir-tree branch that snapped under his hurtling weight. Bruised but unhurt, Murchison clambered on in an uneven descent that was marked by stumbles, curses and painful yells as he hit rocks or received head bumps and scratches from branches. He ended up outside Moody's tent a few minutes later than Horrie, who was lying on the ground chewing on a bone.

'Horrie got the prize, mate, sorry,' Moody said with a sly grin. 'The bone would have been yours, if you had been a tad quicker.'

'Okay, he's quicker,' Murchison agreed with a rueful grin while he struggled to regain his breath, 'but I needed a few goes to get it right.'

'Horrie couldn't blow out a candle,' Moody said, pointing to the dog. 'I'd say he was fitter too.'

'Still reckon I'd be more reliable.'

'Not at night you wouldn't be. Never.'

'What if there's a verbal component to a message? There have been, you know.'

'I'd teach Horrie to bark it,' Moody replied.

'Bullshit!'

'I wouldn't bet on it,' Moody said, reaching down to pat the dog.

Murchison was not sure if Moody was kidding or not. But such was Horrie's reputation, he would not have been surprised if he was capable of doing it.

That night at about 2.45 a.m. Brooker attached a real note to the dog's collar and off he dashed, as sure-footed as if it had been fully daylight. Brooker then fired two pistol shots. This let the patrol at the top of the hill know that their message was on its way to HQ. Horrie found Moody asleep in his tent and licked his face until he stirred and sat up.

'You little ripper, mate!' Moody said and took the note to the sergeant on duty at HQ. Horrie was patted and congratulated and given a titbit of bully beef, which he swallowed in a second. He wanted more.

'He's lost a bit of weight,' the sergeant observed, reaching for a piece of biscuit.

'He has been his stoic self,' Moody said, 'even seems aware that we are doing without and he doesn't complain. He's an inspiration to the Rebels.'

'To all in the battalion!' the sergeant insisted. 'There is no question he saved my life on Greece. I was in my tent asleep. I heard him barking and left, wearing just my underpants and dived for a trench.' The sergeant became a little emotional. 'Those bloody Stukas flattened our area of the camp.' He picked up Horrie and cuddled him. 'Gotta be a monument to this animal put up back home. Must be!'

The sergeant entered a large HQ tent and two minutes later returned with a message to be taken to Brooker. Moody bent down and attached it to the collar. He pointed up the hill and ordered Horrie to 'Find Poppa . . . Go on!' The dog scampered off, then looked back to see if Moody was following. He cocked his head in a questioning pose, ears erect. 'Up to Poppa! . . . Up to Poppa!' Moody repeated. With that, Horrie was away, charging up the hill.

Horrie sent ten messages this way until a few nights later there was an electrical storm accompanied by a powerful wind that blew over tents and caused minor chaos on the island. An urgent message came in from a patrol at the top of the hill at 3.30 a.m. concerning a small boat, possibly containing German scouts and spies, landing further round the coast. This had to be sent to HQ. Brooker judged that Horrie would be blown off the hill and killed, and decided not to send him. But no Rebel could be sent either for the same reason. While Brooker wandered around cursing and trying to secure his tent in the rain, Horrie followed him around, oblivious of the lightning and thunder that normally would worry dogs. He had seen a courier bring the message in and this normally presaged him being ordered down to Moody. Horrie sat in front of him. Brooker looked at him just as lightning struck nearby with a tremendous thunderclap.

'Shit!' Brooker exclaimed. 'That was bloody close!'

Lightning lit up the area. Rebels ran for trenches, with Brooker warning them not to look for cover under big trees. 'They're bloody serious conductors, you know!' he shouted.

'Yeah,' Fitzsimmons called back from under a large olive tree, 'so is bloody Mozart!'

'You won't be so smart when you're fried!' Brooker snarled back. He noticed his little shadow, Horrie. He bent down in the rain, clutching the urgent message and sighed.

'Horrie, mate,' Brooker said, 'you're our only hope with this one.' He tied the note and handkerchief to his collar. Brooker stood and pointed to the bottom of the hill and reached out to pat him, but he was off and running. Brooker moved close to the edge of the sharp drop and looked down. With the intermittent lightning, he caught glimpses of the small, white flash of Horrie careering, zigzagging and leaping his way on his mission, which was accomplished without mishap.

HQ reacted to the message and sent a dozen soldiers to the cove where the boat had been spotted. Ten men, including three Germans and two Italians in civilian clothes, were found sheltering from the storm in a cave close to the water's edge. They were arrested, imprisoned at the town of Chania and charged with espionage activities 'against the Cretan people'.

16

EVACUATION

On the Rebels' ninth day on Crete they were informed they would be evacuated the next day on the 10,000 tonne transport, the *Lossiebank*. It would take them and all others of the 6th Division who were without weapons and equipment. They would not be needed for the big stoush against the invading Germans, which was now imminent. The Rebels were disappointed and not a little guilty about having to leave so many mates in the battalion. Given the option, all would have stayed and fought, even if they only had pistols and knives to battle with. But they had to go. Moody had left the enterprising Horrie to run free on the island and no one, not even the most officious of officers, had protested or told the Rebels they could not keep a dog. But now their arm of the military was on the move again, this time to Port Said, Egypt, Moody could not be sure about reaction to the battalion mascot. It only needed one nasty individual to object to him and he might be left on Crete. Moody did not have the pack that had spirited him everywhere so far. He looked around for something in which to hide him and decided on an ammunition box. The steel frame had small holes punched in the base, but it would be still cramped and challenging for the little animal.

Just when the men were boarding, a low growl emitted from the ammunition box. The Rebels all glanced at each other. Moody opened the box.

'Not now, mate, okay?' Moody whispered with a stern look and glancing at the confused little expression as the lid was shut on him again. His growl continued. Then came the muffled bark. Moody sweated. He glanced around to see if any officer was near.

'Hurry it up, you blokes!' Murchison called. 'The Huns are coming!'

All diggers on the shore and walking up gangways looked up to the skies as the seconds ticked down from Horrie's usual two-minute warning. Just as half the men had boarded the boat, a wave of Stukas rolled over them. Everyone took cover but there was a resolute, almost fatalistic ease to the battalion's reaction. The gunners knew that there was no use panicking or pushing on board. Orderly movements up gangways at the double did not see anyone break ranks and try to scramble on deck. The Luftwaffe always put nerves on edge and often had 'hits' in these

Horrie getting his first bath from Moody after being found in the Libyan desert.

Bill Shegog with the shield he painted for B Co. to decorate the Officers mess.

Horrie receives his winter uniform.

Horrie supervises Moody digging a trench. Later, the dog dropped a big bone in it, thinking that this was its purpose.

Horrie is bemused by music coming from a portable army wireless set.

Aboard the HMAS Defender after being rescued from the bombed and stricken troopship Costa Rica, 27 April 1942.

Horrie and some of his friends in Crete. Standing (l to r) Feathers, Friday Mills, Don Gill. Kneeling (l to r) Murchie, Moody, Arch (later killed), Poppa Brooker, Bash (later killed) and Blue Lyburn.

Horrie howling along with Moody on the mouth-organ at Khassa, Palestine (Israel).

Horrie in Syria on the toboggan built for him.

Horrie in the Vichy tank found on his hunting trip in Syria with Moody and Gill.

1941. Tiberias. Palestine. Horrie starts on a desert journey.

Horrie in his 'uniform'. It was made for him to beat the cold in Syria.

The stern of the *West Point*, carrying the American flag. This converted liner took the 2/1 Machine Gun Battalion from the Middle East back to Australia.

Horrie at the Australian Soldiers Club Tel Aviv. The diggers include Rebels, Fitzsimmons (second from left), and next to him, Harlor and Gill.

A 2/1 Machine Gunners doing guard duty with Horrie.

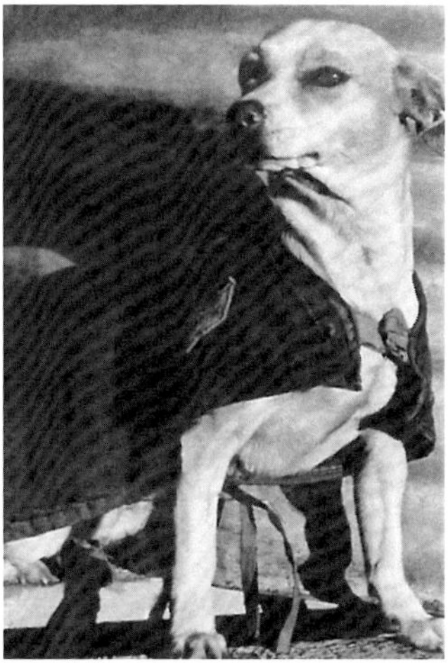

Imshi. She was the 2/1 Anti -Tank Regiment's mascot and Horrie's companion in the Middle East.

Horrie and Jim Moody on top of a Syrian mountain. The Lebanon Valley is beyond them.

Horrie is in this pack on Don Gill's back when they were about to board *West Point* which would take them to Australia. Moody took the picture and stayed close, encouraging Horrie to remain still and quiet.

Some of the Rebels with Horrie in Syria playing keepings-off game, which he initiated to keep him warm.

Horrie, Don Gill and Moodie in Tel Aviv, 14 February.

At Zubaydat, Aussies and locals playing two-up.

Horrie resting beneath the aft gun on *Lossiebank* during evacuation from Crete.

Horrie in his pack.

Horrie confronts an Arab, soon after a Stuka bombed the 2/1 Machine Gunners' camp at Dier Suneid, Palestine, leaving bomb craters.

Dog tired: Horrie sleeps alongside Moody in Crete.

Horrie's beach shelter near Tel Aviv. He had a busy day guarding the Rebels' clothes from mischievous Arab boys.

Horrie on guard outside the Rebels' tent, Dier Suneid, Palestine, August 1941.

Horrie was given this set of harness, complete with colour patch, in recognition of his faithful service in Greece and Crete. His identification disk was made from a Greek Drack coin engraved with H.Moody VXO1.

Imshi (left) with Horrie.

Horrie with a querulous look, which was a feature when he concentrated on the whine of in-coming German planes.

A typical Middle Eastern coffee house.

Author Ion Idriess meets Horrie. He would never know that Horrie survived.

Moody with trademark pipe and camera.

Moody and Imshi II with whom Horrie sired seven pups.

Moody with second wife Joan. They married in 1951 and had three children.

Horrie in Syria guarding equipment while the Rebels were employed making roads.

Jim Moody examining an ancient coin he had just purchased. He believed it was from the era of Roman Rule, 64 BC to 323 AD.

Imshi II, the Scottish Terrier from a Sydney dog pound, with three of her pups sired by Horrie.

Moody with good friend and fellow Rebel, Don Gill.

strikes, but the element of surprise of them roaring down was not the shock it had been. There was also a strong battery of anti-aircraft guns on board and on the shore, which gave some protection. Horrie's barks were drowned by the howling planes that careered at the vulnerable *Lossiebank.* Three bombs landed close, throwing a dozen soldiers into the water. Once on board, Moody headed for the gun deck with the ammunition box, the one place it would not look unusual. He shoved it under a tarpaulin and sat near it. He kept talking under his breath to Horrie, trying to reassure him and also keep him quiet. A ship's officer, Captain Burke, noticed Moody sitting there, apparently gibbering to himself.

'You all right, Private?' he asked.

'Arh, arh no, well yes . . . not really, sir,' Moody mumbled, 'it's the bombs, sir . . .'

Just as he spoke there was an almighty crunch as a bomb landed on the wharf, luckily 50 metres from the last soldiers hurrying on board. Its impact shook the ship and sent several men into the water. The officer lost his footing and his cap went flying.

'Noth—nothing to worry about, Private!' Captain Burke said in shaky voice. 'Pull yourself together and get . . . get . . . going!'

'Yes, sir, thank you, sir. Your words are very sustaining, sir,' Moody said, putting on a trembling act.

The officer regained his cap and added: 'You have shell shock, Private Mooney!'

'Moody, sir.'

'Who me?' Burke snapped. 'Don't be insolent!'

'No, *Moody* is my name, sir, not *Mooney*.'

Stukas attacked again and sent Captain Burke dashing below deck. The noise covered up Horrie's burst of sustained barking. Moody lifted the tarpaulin, opened the box and tried to calm him down as the ship hastened to make its exit from the harbour. But Horrie was agitated. Moody opened his only remaining tin of bully beef and gave the dog a morsel, which distracted and comforted him. A half-hour later, when the Luftwaffe's interest in the ship had abated for the moment and the *Lossiebank* was well out to sea, Moody released Horrie. He was safe, at least from being abandoned on Crete.

There were no more attacks in the next 24 hours and although the ship was on full alert, most on board believed that the Luftwaffe would not attack again. The *Lossiebank* was moving out of range for persistent attacks, although they were not technically outside the bombers' range. The conventional wisdom was that the Luftwaffe would not waste fuel on travelling out to sea for a one-off attack. Yet still the Rebels kept one eye on Horrie, just in case. On the second day, he was wandering around the deck when he took up his sitting position. He cocked his head in the familiar pose so seared into the minds of every member of the battalion. His face creased; his head moved into different positions as if he were a mechanical toy. Then the ears began to stiffen. It was enough for the Rebels. Even before the ears stood up without a flicker, they were shouting that everyone should take cover. Horrie's low guttural utterance developed into a growl. Then he barked and began to jump about. Hundreds of men, who until a second ago had been lounging on the deck, began running. The *Lossiebank*'s anti-aircraft guns swung into position as directed by those watching Horrie. Moody dashed to scoop him up but he had scuttled away. Moody rushed around but in the confusion Horrie could not be found. Moody scurried to steps that would take him below deck. All the Rebels were there, skulking about, annoyed and frustrated that they had no weapons with which to fight back as they had on board the *Costa Rica.*

'Where's Horrie?' several of them asked Moody.

'He'll be in a safe spot on deck. Couldn't find him.'

They braced for the bombs. They shook the ship but none did damage. They heard the strafing just as the ship's defensive weapons poured plenty back at the 20 or so Stukas. A 30 second silence was followed by a second run and then a third. Then the squadron of planes disappeared into the sun. Horrie stopped barking. The ship's guns fell silent. The soldiers began relaxing, rolling cigarettes, smoking pipes, playing cards and swapping yarns. A cricket bat and tennis ball were produced but there was not enough room for a game on the crowded deck. Instead, a rugby ball was thrown around until a digger with huge hands hurled the ball so hard, American football-style, that it sailed into the sea. Soldiers one by one, or in groups of two or three, began to approach the Rebels, asking to see Horrie. No one had seen him. A half-hour later, he appeared limping and bleeding from his right shoulder.

Moody, Brooker, Gill and Fitzsimmons rushed to him. The blood was wiped away to reveal a long, thin steel bomb splinter that was embedded under his skin. He was not distressed and seemed happy at the attention. Brooker held him, while Moody pinched the skin surrounding the splinter and spoke to him affectionately as Gill used a pocketknife to ease the sliver out. The wound was cleaned and dressed. Horrie continued to limp but it did not impede his activity or the enjoyment of so many soldiers wanting to meet him, pat him, shake his paw or be photographed with him.

'All we need is Horrietta to nurse him back to full health,' Fitzsimmons remarked. Horrie's ears pricked up at the mention of his 'lost' companion.

Moody put his forefinger to his lips and frowned at Fitzsimmons.

'The "etta" word is not to be mentioned. Makes him nostalgic.'

'Sorry,' Fitzsimmons said, 'but remember, nostalgia isn't what it used to be.'

The soldiers disembarked at Port Said, on Egypt's Mediterranean coast, built in 1859 for the construction of the Suez Canal. There was no inspection but just in case, the Rebels crowded around Moody carrying Horrie, but no officer noticed. The soldiers were herded onto a train. Moody let Horrie run free, but he could not move too far in the crowded carriages. Yet he didn't seem to want to. His wound troubled him. He stretched his neck in an attempt to tear off the dressing. Moody removed it.

Horrie began to lick the wound, and just when he seemed preoccupied with it, instinct had him alert. He jumped over Fitzsimmons and Harlor to bark and growl at Arabs by the side of the track. The wound was forgotten. Horrie was more interested once more in displaying his attitude to the locals in Middle Eastern garb.

*

They changed trains at Kantara on the canal and began to cross the Sinai Desert. It brought back memories for Brooker. He commented on the effort of the Anzac troopers in the desert in World War I as the train passed through the village of Romani, telling them: 'The 1500 troopers under Harry Chauvel defeated a 25,000-strong Turkish army right here in the Battle of Romani on 4 August 1916.'

'That's odds of 17 to 1,' Murchison said with a trace of scepticism

'What were you,' Fitzsimmons asked, 'supermen?'

'Not really. We had horses. That made the difference. For what it is worth, that Anzac victory saved Egypt as a British Empire mandate.' Brooker paused, looked out the window as Horrie barked a short disapproval, and then added with a sigh, 'Not worth much today, I'll grant you, because here we are in the same bloody desert fighting the same bloody enemy, essentially. But it was big then.'

'I thought you were on the Western Front under Monash?' Fitzsimmons said.

'No. I just know the history, you callow youth, you! We all ended up here in 1916 after Gallipoli, before the

Australian army was split from the Light Horse, who stayed here and defeated the Turks. I was in one of the regiments. By 1918 we'd knocked them out of the Middle East for the first time in 400 years.' He poised to stare at Murchison before adding with emphasis, '*for what it's worth today*.'

'You're living in the past, old man,' Murchison said.

'But it's a past that fortifies me, inspires me,' Brooker said, 'and it should do that for you too. But you are pig-ignorant of it.'

Brooker and Murchison tended to be fractious in their disagreements but it was all in the interests of the favourite digger pastime of 'knocking,' or abrasive, good-natured ridicule, which an individual had to counter verbally or accept with a grin.

'Is this where Bill the Bastard . . . you know, won a horse VC or something?' Harlor asked as he tinkered with a piece of equipment.

'Correct,' Brooker replied, 'go to the top of a rather average Rebel class.' He looked down at Horrie. 'Pardon me, Horrie. Gordie goes to second place after you, of course!' The dog wagged his tail, more for being mentioned rather than comprehension. 'Bill was a grand Waler, biggest by weight, and the bravest of the 200,000 neddies we sent here to fight the Turks. He didn't get a VC, although he should have. His rider, the legendary Michael Shanahan, got the DSO for his efforts in that battle. But if you were looking for one individual standout performer in six hours of fighting on that fateful night of

4 August 1916 it was Bill. When some troopers were going through ten horses, he just ran on and on. Shanahan said he covered the equivalent of 20 Melbourne Cups, with one break to bring five troopers on his back out of the front.'

Most of the Rebels had heard Brooker tell his story before. But no one interrupted him. They were captivated as their train rattled slowly on, especially when he pointed out the mountains of sand around which the Battle of Romani took place. The tale came to life.

'Has the area changed much?' Moody asked.

'Yes, a lot,' Brooker said, pointing to vines and crops cultivated on neat farms. 'Never saw that sort of thing then. It was just rough, inhospitable desert. Now you've got towns and this train running through it, along with a water pipeline that admittedly was begun in 1916 because of the war then.'

'Makes you think we should do it back home in the north and the outback,' Moody observed. 'There is a worse desert here than in Australia.'

The others nodded their agreement. The train rumbled on through the Sinai and into Palestine and a camp at Dier Suneid, which appealed to the Australians. It featured orange groves, whose green foliage contrasted with the one-spectrum yellow sand. The groves were surrounded by deep green cactus, which was clipped and under control in contrast to the growth nearer the coast at the ancient fortress city of Gaza where it grew wild and created substantial 'walls.' On arrival, Brooker talked of the final battle for Gaza, and the Australian mounted charge of 31 October 1917 at Beersheba, 70 kilometres further inland.

'Greatest mounted charge in history by our boys,' he said.

'Hang on,' Gill challenged him, 'what about Napoleon? He had many thousands of cavalrymen in his charges. There were only 800 in the Australian 4th Brigade at Beersheba.'

'I stick by what I said,' Brooker retorted. 'Napoleon only had to outnumber his opponents with men, horses and swords—the Austrians or whomever—and he won. The bookies wouldn't take bets on him! But our boys charged against 4500 entrenched Turks, artillery, machine gunners, snipers, not to forget the Hun air force rolling out bombs on them. They were the longest shot bet of that war. Their charge took courage of the highest kind and they triumphed.'

'I agree with Poppa on that one,' Moody said. 'I want to take photos at Beersheba.'

The Rebels were united for the first since the Western Desert when Bill Shegog turned up at the camp having recovered from his motorbike accident. Big Jim Hewitt, who'd been ill, was also there. The reunion called for a celebration. Both men had heard about Horrie's exploits and they thought he was skinnier.

'We tend to think of him as "athletic,"' Fitzsimmons said deadpan as he patted a very pleased Horrie, who seemed happier than anyone that all his team was back together. Hewitt made sure that he was given a big feed of scraps from the officers' mess. He feasted on them, much to the envy of the Rebels, who were adamant that the officer 'left-overs' were far superior to their own monotonous food.

The Arabs in the region seemed friendly enough but the Australians were forewarned to chain their rifles in the tents as they had in Libya, and told not to leave valuables there. If anything the locals were bigger thieves than in the Western Desert. The diggers in both wars never adjusted to the Arab way of claiming anything that was not bolted or chained down as theirs. On their second day at this camp, a pucker, lean visiting British officer with a trim Hitler-like moustache lectured the Australians about 'tolerance' and remembering to appreciate that Palestine was the Arabs' land and that 'you are all seen as invaders, whether British or Hun or Italian.'

'Excuse me, sir,' Murchison interrupted him, 'but how do Arabs deal with other Arabs who steal things? Do they show tolerance?'

'That is not the point, Private!' the officer snapped. 'And don't interrupt again!'

'No, sir, of course not, sir, but we have been told that the Arabs chop off the hands of fellow Arabs who steal—'

'And they chop off something else if they thieve their wives!' Fitzsimmons chimed in, much to the mirth of the assembled gunners.

The seething officer put them both on charges of insubordination (which were later dismissed after Hewitt's intervention).

Without having to be told, Horrie took it upon himself to guard the Rebels' tent. One evening when they were all absent and in the mess hall, he patiently sat outside the tent roped to a pole, his head resting on his paws, and one eye on the passing parade. As darkness fell, two young Arab youths sneaked up on the tent. Horrie leapt and caught one by the leg. His needle-sharp teeth bit deep into the youth's calf. He screamed in agony and just managed to crawl clear of Horrie. The youths fled, leaving a trail of blood. Horrie was furious. He tried to bite his way through the rope, but gave up. He was still agitated when the Rebels returned, but his mood changed to one of joy. Later, they were told of his defence of the tent by other battalion members who witnessed his efforts.

'I wish we had him for our tent,' one gunner remarked, 'we've had two damned rifles stolen in a week!'

*

News reached the Rebels in mid-May 1941 that Murchison's mates Archie and Bash had been killed at one of the key battle-points on Crete, Maleme airfield. They had been fighting in a New Zealand contingent against the incoming waves of German paratroopers. Murchison took it hard. He had survivor's guilt for not staying on the island with the courageous Kiwis. They had been set to leave but at the last minute decided to stay and join the several thousand New Zealanders still on Crete in what may have been last stands against the enemy. Murchison's mood changed from his usual cheerful self to one of solitary anger. Often he only wanted Horrie's company. The dog gave him unconditional affection without trite conversation, which was ideal for Murchison's state of mind. After a few days of this, he sprang to life when the group was told that the village of Dier Suneid was off limits.

'Bugger that!' he said. 'Are we Rebels or what?'

'I don't think you boys should go near it,' Brooker said, shaking his head. 'The women are really beautiful but dangerous and beguiling. They know how to do the dance of the seven veils in the ancient art of seduction.'

'Dangerous? Why?' Murchison asked.

'Might have disease; syphilis, for instance.'

'Arh, that's bullshit. Old wives' tales from the last war. We've all got rubbers.'

'Careful, Murchie!' Fitzsimmons said in mock warning. 'You can't erase syphilis. Stays with you, *indelibly* for the rest of a shortened life.'

'You blokes are chicken!' Murchison sneered.

'Okay; don't say I didn't warn you,' Brooker said, before his face creased slowly into a wry grin. 'But perhaps I should come along, you know, in case there's trouble.'

'No thanks,' Murchison said, 'wouldn't want you to catch something.'

*

That evening when it was still light, Horrie was tied to the tent pole again.

'Can't take you, old mate,' Gill told him, 'your prejudice against the locals rules you out.'

Horrie barked in protest but to no avail as Moody, Gill, Murchison and Featherstone walked to Dier Suneid, almost hidden on the road to Gaza by an orange grove that cactus threatened to engulf. It was surrounded by a two metre mud-brick wall, which had only one narrow, rickety gate entrance. The four 'tourists' entered and walked down a lane so narrow that the mud-brick buildings either side seemed to merge into a dead end. They passed several Arabs. Two camels and their minders brushed by going the other way. The lane meandered on until widening under stone archways and leading to homes with small front yards. It ended at a town centre with a square no bigger than two tennis courts. Urchins kicked a mottled soccer ball and dodged and weaved among donkeys, dogs, chickens and two camels. There were about 20 stalls doing a slow trade with a few Arabs and a handful of British soldiers. The still-lingering heat of the day and alien, mingling smells of sewage, dung, food being cooked and other aromas that the Rebels could not distinguish had them screwing up their noses. Locals eyed them with curiosity. Ringing the square was an assortment of shops, all in need of repair and selling unappetising fruit, vegetables and an odd assortment of toys and figurines. Several Arabs sat under the awning of a cafe that sold coffee and cakes. Murchison was first to notice women in long dresses inside the dimly lit cafe.

'Hey,' he whispered to Moody, 'those girls are not wearing the traditional head garb. Their faces are uncovered. They're not the "dusky maidens" Brooker conjured for us. They're more "mature," I'd say, but they look pretty sexy!'

'Yeah, not quite as Brooker described,' Moody agreed, 'but they're on the game for sure.'

Featherstone and Gill warned Murchison not to venture in.

'Just look at the wogs with them,' Moody said, 'cutthroat types. We don't want any trouble. Leave it be.'

'No, bugger it,' Murchison mumbled, 'I'm going to see what's what. I keep thinking of Archie and Bash. You never know when your number's up.'

Noticing the hesitation, one of the men in the cafe stood and beckoned Murchison in. He had a short beard and wore a headdress and clean white robes with gold inlay lining. Three other Arabs looked on with vacant expressions, while a couple played a board game in one corner.

'Looks like Lawrence of Arabia wants to offer you a cigarette,' Fitzsimmons said, 'and maybe something else.'

The Arab in well-pressed clothes smiled, exposing one lonely tooth. He motioned his hand at the three women, all in their late thirties or early forties. Murchison wandered in. The others sat down and ordered coffee. One of the women served them. She was tall, with wide hips, and she showed ample cleavage under a green blouse. Murchison offered the Arab an English cigarette, which he accepted. The Arab grinned and asked him in fractured English if he would like to smoke a pipe with him.

'Don't get too cosy with the boss cocky, Murchie,' Moody warned, 'never know what they're offering.'

'It's their kind of tobacco,' Murchison said, and then, addressing the Arab, asked, 'Tobacco, right?'

The Arab smiled and nodded. The tall woman stepped forward holding a saffron-coloured substance, about the size of a golf ball, in her hands. She placed it on a small table and began preparing a decorated silver pipe with a black mouthpiece. The woman placed the saffron ball on some charcoal in a large bowl on the table. She handed the pipe to the Arab who held the end of it close to the ball and commenced to suck. The charcoal embers glowed; the ball's edges became tinged with brown as the Arab inhaled the smoke. When it was drawn well, he handed the pipe to Murchison, who nodded and accepted it. Despite Moody's protests, Murchison was intrigued to try this 'Arab-style tobacco.' The woman looked on with interest. As Murchison inhaled, she too smiled for the first time. She sat on the chair next to him, one elbow on her knee and her chin cupped in her hand as if she was fascinated by his reaction. The other two women moved close too. Murchison liked the result. His face relaxed. After a third round of inhaling, his expression lightened further. He had a beatific smile.

'Hmm,' he said with a delighted, questioning expression, 'never had tobacco like this before.' The others were preoccupied with their coffee. Fitzsimmons rolled himself a cigarette, after refusing the Arab's offer to make his own variety for him. The Rebels sipped the black coffee in tiny cups and it reminded them of the Greek-style offerings that they all liked. They commented on the more bitter taste. They added sugar lumps and munched on the cakes, which tasted like halva, the sesame sweet that they had enjoyed on Crete. Moody smoked his pipe and mulled over a perplexing, pocket-sized book, *Arabic for One Shilling*. He tried speaking to the other Arabs. One stared ahead as if he had not been addressed. This response made Moody think his pronunciation had to be terrible. He spoke to a second man, who seemed startled and shook his head.

'Is it my bloody accent?' Moody mumbled to himself as he tried to memorise 'hello,' 'pleased to meet you,' and 'good morning.' Seeing his difficulty, a sultry female with outsized brown eyes wandered over, beckoned to him to give her the book, and then examined it. Without a word, she tossed it back to him with what seemed a disdainful glance and then walked away with a languid swing of the hips. She sat on a bar-stool inside the cafe, lit a cigarette and then smiled seductively at Moody, who resumed his language 'study.' He was uncomfortable in this indulgence of Murchison's whim, and none of the other Rebels could relax. A group of boys gathered in an attempt to sell them other food items. The Arab owner waved a dismissive hand at them, but the boys pressed closer.

'Jeez!' Murchison muttered with a confused expression after his sixth turn at the pipe. 'Is this a bloody earthquake or what?!'

He tried to stand but couldn't. He fell back in his chair. His face was pale. He made a second struggling effort to stand. His feet wouldn't obey his brain's simple command.

'Reckon I'm gunna chuck,' Murchison uttered as he finally made it to his feet and stumbled into the street and vomited. Moody walked to the charcoal bowl and looked down at the now brown ball, which was almost absorbed into the charcoal. The grinning Arab boss handed him the pipe, with a gesture indicating he should try it. Moody sniffed the end of it and blinked an understanding. The unfamiliar odour made him cough. Just at that moment, Horrie burst into the square at the double, growling and snapping at any local in sight. He made a beeline for the boys outside the cafe.

'Let's go!' Moody said before chasing Horrie. The dog latched onto the trouser leg of a boy who tried to retreat and only managed to see the fabric ripped away. The Arab at the cafe gesticulated, indicating the Rebels had to pay for the food, drink and smoke. Horrie ducked away from Moody and turned his attention to the Arabs in the cafe, who backed inside as the dog barked and snarled. In the commotion, Gill and Fitzsimmons had helped Murchison out of the square and down the tight alley to the gate. Moody managed to grab Horrie, tuck him under his arm and hurry with Featherstone after the others. Urged on by the Arabs in the cafe, the boys followed, throwing stones at the Rebels, who hastened out the only gate entrance and away down the road.

Moody dared not let go of Horrie. His eyes were on fire. The hackles on his back were up. He wriggled, growled and kept glancing back at the boys who had followed them a short distance, still urged on by the Arabs from the cafe, who stayed near the gate. But with a number of other diggers and English soldiers walking past in both directions, all the village locals soon disappeared back through the gate.

'Saved by Horrie yet again,' Fitzsimmons exclaimed and when everyone, except the dazed Murchison, patted Horrie, he calmed down. He had gnawed his way through the rope attached to the tent pole, an act they assumed he had performed on Crete.

'What happened to you?' Gill asked Murchison. 'Something you ate last night?'

'No,' Moody informed them, 'that smoke Lawrence of Arabia gave Murchie was opium.'

*

Murchison was in a state of 'wellbeing' as the effects of his ingestion lingered for more than two days. When he recovered he told the Rebels he wanted to go back to the village and 'shoot bloody Lawrence of Arabia.'

'Aw, c'mon, Murchie,' Fitzsimmons chided, 'you just want a big packet of what went into that special pipe. You've been smiling benignly ever since.'

The others laughed.

'Yeah,' Featherstone agreed, 'never seen you so generous and with such bonhomie.'

Murchison managed a smile of resignation. He had no response, for he admitted that the opium had relaxed every muscle, and thought.

'Can see why the bloody stuff is so addictive,' he said with a rueful look, 'a few of the diggers have succumbed over here.' He frowned. 'You know, I've been thinking—'

'A very dangerous side-effect of opium,' Fitzsimmons said.

'No seriously, I want action. I can't stand sweating in the heat here, getting listless and bored. The whisper is that some of the battalion are putting in for transfers to the 2/3 Machine Gun Battalion. They are set for action in Syria. We are set to fight the Vichy French any day now. Our General Stan Savige is having a big say in that affair. The Allies don't want the Nazis using their control over the Frogs, who have a mandate over Syria and the Lebanon, as a springboard for attacking Egypt. So it's on in Syria, boys.'

'Stan is a fine commander,' Brooker said with an approving nod. 'He looks after all his boys. You'll be in good hands. Stan's one of our greatest soldier-commanders.' He shook his head and after a pause added: 'To think we are going to fight the French after all the blood we spilt for them in the last war! I'll never get over it.'

'You must forgive them, Poppa,' Moody said, 'it was either collaborate with the Nazis or see Paris smashed and millions more Frogs die.'

'Would you turn-coat like the Vichy French under Premier bloody Marshal Petain?' Brooker asked.

'No, but we don't know all the circumstances.'

'Bulldust!' Brooker said.

In late May 1941, a few days later, Murchison managed a transfer to the other Machine Gun Battalion (the 2/3), which was bound for Syria and a battle there in June 1941. This move did not herald a major splitting of the group, but it was a sad day when he was about to march out. Murchison made a fuss of Horrie. The dog knew something was up. He bounced around Murchison, who tried to ignore him as he prepared to leave the tent.

'When we've cleaned up the Frogs,' he said after shaking hands with each man, 'I'll be back. I am already looking forward to that reunion.' He paused to look down at Horrie, whose head was at its enquiring tilt, 'especially with you, mate.' He moved out. Horrie followed him for a few paces before sitting and watching him depart with nearly the intensity he demonstrated when he heard German planes in the distance. The dog whined a little and would not move from his vigil for an hour in the hope that Murchison would return.

*

The Germans defeated the Allies in Greece and Crete in May and June 1941 but, in a Dunkirk-like operation, 43,000 Allied soldiers were saved, although much heavy equipment, including artillery guns, was captured by the Germans. Most analysis blamed the loss on the enemy's all-round superiority in tank and aircraft numbers. The Allies had about a quarter of their numbers in each field, in a situation made worse by the British not having access to airfields, which rendered the air force impotent.

The 2/1 Gunners suffered. They had 104 casualties including 77 men who were taken prisoner, and the Rebels realised how lucky they had been to escape capture, wounding or death.

17

NUMBER ONE WARRIOR

One night early in June 1941, Horrie became agitated as he lay under the blanket at the foot of Moody's bed. Thinking he was having a dream or nightmare, which the dog often did, Moody rolled over and tried to return to sleep. But a second later Horrie was up and growling. The entire tent stirred.

'What's wrong with him?' Gordie asked, annoyed at being disturbed. 'There are no bloody Huns flying around here!'

Moody got out of bed and noticed Horrie's ears. They were focused.

'Stukas!' Moody exclaimed. 'Everybody for the trenches! Quick!'

That led to a mad scramble. Horrie was first out, scuttling for the nearest slit trench. But he almost skidded to a stop en route near the butcher's tent. He barked, whirled around and barked several times more, and then darted off. The burly butcher came stumbling out. He heard the warning cries from the Rebels and saw the battalion in chaos as gunners raced for cover in every direction, and decided that he too should take evasive action. Then the Stuka 'siren' was heard above the warning beeps from the camp's tannoy system. A minute later three bombs thudded to ground, creating asymmetrical craters. After the Henkel-escorted Stuka had done its damage, the shaken butcher returned to his tent, but could not find it. Confused in the dark, he wandered around until his torch shone on the area where he swore his tent had been, close to the trees where the soldiers' mess was located. In its place was a deep hole where one of the bombs had struck. Little pieces of torn tent fabric were all that remained. The butcher felt he was still in some weird nightmare as his jumbled mind retraced the events of the previous 12 minutes. He had been woken by Horrie, whose bark had been so urgent and loud that he seemed to have been in the tent with him. This led to the butcher rolling out of bed, when he became more cognisant of the situation and the potential peril from the night sky. On reflection, he was in no doubt that his special little mate, who visited the kitchen often looking for meat scraps, had saved his life. From then on, he dedicated himself to making sure Horrie was the best fed soldier in the camp.

During breakfast the Rebels put Horrie on a chain purloined from the transport section to stop him from biting through rope and making a nuisance of himself in the cook-house. They brought him back cooked meat scraps so that he would never go without, but soon discovered that he was chomping into some raw meat that none of them had given him.

'How did the little devil manage that?' a bewildered Gill asked. No one had an answer.

'Perhaps we should rename him Horrie Houdini,' Fitzsimmons remarked.

Later in the day, Moody visited the cook-house and spoke to the butcher.

'I gave it to him,' the butcher, Barry Bain, admitted. 'During the day when you blokes are on a detail I visit the tent with a decent cut. That little bastard saved my life the night that rogue Stuka hit us. I'm gunna repay him every day. I love him!'

'You say you give it to him every day. When exactly?'

'Aw, 'bout lunch time, why?'

'Not at breakfast mess time?'

'No, I'm always flat-out preparing your meals.'

'He's always chewing on meat when we get back from mess . . .'

'You know why, don't you? Horrie wants to be one of your team, even if he can't accompany you to the mess. He must bury the meat that I give him close to the pole where you tie him up. Then he must dig it up to have a feed when you are having breakfast.'

Moody just shook his head in amazement.

'I know what you're thinking,' the butcher said, swinging a cleaver into a side of beef, 'he's the smartest animal you've ever come across.'

'That is what I was thinking!'

'I swear he is smarter than half the battalion. I really do.'

Moody was about to leave the tent kitchen when the butcher wiped the cleaver on his apron and said with a frown: 'I don't know if I dreamt this or not. But it felt like Horrie was actually in my tent just before those bombs hit the other night. His bark was so loud and close. Is that my imagination playing tricks or what?'

'Not really. I was following him after he gave his usual warning. He hesitated at your tent, did a kind of spin and then he raced on. He jumped close to your door. I know him better than anyone. He was singling your tent out for a special warning!'

The butcher had played first-grade Rugby League. He was big and solid, befitting a man whose speciality was prop, and who dealt in slaughter and meat. His eyes welled up. He tried hard to hide his feelings and mumbled: 'That little bastard!' he said, holding back tears and clearing his throat. 'I'd take a bullet for him, I really would.'

'Mate, you and all the Rebels too . . . and plenty more . . .'

'I'd put my money on nearly the whole fuckin' battalion defending him.' The butcher paused and added the verbal tic that punctuated half his utterances: 'I *really* would!'

The next day Horrie was seen with his biggest ever bone, which was a reward from the grateful butcher. The dog decided not to bury this one and only let it alone for an hour to watch Moody digging a slit trench near the tent. He sat eyeing every shovel movement with intense interest as if he approved of the idea of more protection and cover after the surprise air attack of the night before. Fitzsimmons was so taken by Horrie's fascination with the digging enterprise that he took a picture of him overseeing Moody's excavations.

'Got to have that shot for posterity,' Fitzsimmons said, 'because otherwise no one would believe Horrie's capacity for prolonged concentration!'

That night Horrie tried to take the huge bone into Moody's bed but it was too big for him to lift. He kept looking at his prime 'master' and wagging his tail, 'trying to enlist my aid in this matter,' Moody wrote. When Horrie received no assistance, he dragged the bone out of the tent. Fitzsimmons crept behind him to see what he would do with it. Horrie managed to drop it into the slit trench.

'Well I'll be buggered!' Fitzsimmons said to Moody. 'That's why he was so mesmerised by you digging the trench. He thought you were doing it for him to put his bone in!'

*

The next day Horrie went missing. His absence was not noted during the day for he often went AWL during daylight hours, always to return in the evening. But as night fell, the Rebels became concerned. At midnight they went to nearby camps but to no avail. The following day, the Rebels searched every camp within a 20 kilometre radius, showing his picture. Some claimed to have seen a dog like him here and there, but there were no specifics, only vague recollections. After eight days they feared the worst.

'Got to face it,' Shegog said to the others as he paused from a portrait of Gill, 'you've seen the number of dead animals beside the road. We know how thick the traffic is—'

'And how thick the speed-merchant bus-drivers are,' Fitzsimmons said.

'You're suggesting he's road kill?' Gill asked with a sigh.

''Fraid I am, mate,' Shegog said, sipping from a whisky flask, 'sorry.'

A day later Gill went on leave with others from the Rebels' platoon to the relatively modern city of Tel Aviv on the coast 85 kilometres north of Gaza. Jews from nearby Jaffa, which was populated by Arabs, had built Tel Aviv on sand dunes in about 1910 to give themselves a separate location.

The group from the platoon had just finished visiting some historic landmarks and was on the way to a fish cafe not far from a rubbish tip on the beach across the road. All heads turned at the sound of a dog's bark. It was Horrie scampering from the tip in their direction. With little heed for the traffic, he darted across the road and leapt at Gill, nearly knocking him over in his excitement. The group was shocked at his condition. He was emaciated and covered in filth from the tip. His fur was in tufts created by tar and oil.

'Jesus Christ, Horrie!' Gill said, picking him up despite his condition. 'You haven't smelt this bad since you dived into that latrine in Greece!'

Gill would not let him go until they bought him a new lead and collar. Horrie was then fed with a chicken sandwich and taken to Tel Aviv's Australian Soldiers' Club where he was cleaned up. The group adjourned to the bar to celebrate Horrie's return to the battalion. Two roof fans whirred. A sweating, blind accordion player near an open window was performing 'The White Cliffs of Dover,' accompanied by a young female violinist.

'Beers all round,' Gill said, putting money on the counter.

'Not for the wee doggie, I hope,' a Scots barman said, eyeing Horrie's condition. 'He could do wi' a wee spot of brandy and a wee cow.'

The gunners laughed.

'A pot of milk wouldn't go astray for starters,' Gill suggested.

*

Murchison joined the 2/3 Machine Gun Battalion, with its four companies from South Australia, Victoria, Tasmania and Western Australia, which had only arrived at the Suez Canal in mid-May 1941. He became attached to it when it travelled to Palestine, where it joined Australia's 7th

Division, which was preparing to invade Syria on 8 June. Less than five weeks later in the second week of July 1941, the successful campaign was over when the Vichy French were surrounded and a ceasefire came into operation at midnight on 11 July. Rumours reached the gunners' camp that the fighting had been fierce and the Rebels became concerned about Murchison. When no word reached them, some thought the worst but did not mention their fears. Brooker had drilled into them his belief that negative thoughts fuelled negative energy.

'Stay positive about young Murchie,' Brooker advised. 'You couldn't kill him with a crowbar. He'll make it.'

*

Horrie's continued heroics caused the Rebels to give him a special 'treat' on their first trip on the narrow but passable road to Jerusalem. He led the team onto a local bus as if he were a veteran on some special mission.

'Horrie showed a certain aplomb getting on board,' Moody observed. 'I wouldn't mind betting that's how he reached Tel Aviv.'

The Rebels took up the remaining half-dozen seats in the bus that held 30 troops. Moody, Gill and some of the others knew no fear when driving at breakneck speed on their motorbikes, but when it came to others driving them, it was a different matter.

Gill felt that the Arab drivers seemed to send up a prayer for themselves and perhaps the others in the bus and then accelerate. Any other vehicle blasting a horn in order to pass, seemed to be taken as a signal by the drivers, not to give way, but to start a race.

Much to the dismay of Moody and Gill, the other Rebels and diggers, led by Fitzsimmons, and a drunken Shegog, encouraged the driver by yelling: 'Let her go, George!' But it was a superfluous urging. The driver was determined not to let anyone pass, even, it seemed, to the point of crashing, if the remnants of a score of smashed vehicles on the side of the road and down steep embankments were any guide. At one point a same-sized bus drew level with them. They were close enough to graze each other and it left no room at all for any oncoming traffic. With diggers in both vehicles shouting at the drivers to 'win' the race, Moody and Gill were more afraid than they had ever been doing motorbike somersaults.

It seemed that the adrenalin rush was needed at every opportunity for men at war. They lived on the edge and liked the game of chance, even if a loss could mean death. And Horrie, in his own way, was not dissimilar. In the bus, he had his paws on the window and was panting in the heat, but there was pleasure in his snarling and growling as a kaleidoscope of his most unfavoured people rushed by him on the side of the road and in villages. The bus was moving so fast that he didn't have time to bark before a new blur of local villages and nomads flashed in and out of view. He voiced a low whine of frustration, but in a perverse way he appeared to enjoy it, if the perpetual motion of his tail stump was anything to go by.

Much to the relief of Moody and Gill, the bus ride

shifted from dangerous to hazardous and then hectic as they came closer to the Holy City. Some of the troops in the bus remarked with disgust at the sight of carts loaded with fruit and vegetables pulled by skeletal, struggling horses. In each case, a man rode on the cart and women, bearing loads on their backs, walked alongside or behind, sometimes with children.

'Get over it,' an older digger told a young gunner in a gruff voice. 'We saw this in the last war and some of us tried to rectify matters.'

'How?' the young digger responded.

'We rearranged the seating set-up,' the older digger rasped, 'women and children on the cart, man carrying the load.' He grunted a laugh. 'Got us into big trouble in Cairo, I can tell ya. See, it's their way, their tradition.'

'It's bloody wrong,' the young gunner replied.

'Get over it,' the older digger repeated.

The bus had been slowed by the traffic enough for the Rebels to discuss what they planned for Horrie. After the challenging ride, they first bought him a new harness and lead, the latter being a sturdy mix of wire and rope that he could not chew through, or at least that was the hope, given his needle-sharp incisors. Second, they had made a name tag, or more appropriately in the American vernacular, a 'dog-tag.' It was fashioned from a Greek two-drachma coin, which was inscribed with his name, number and unit: 'Horace, EX.1 2/1 M/G Bn.'

The EX.1 signified that Horrie was the Gunners' number one warrior from Egypt, but this could have applied to Greece, Crete and Palestine. The unit colour patch and the coin were attached to the harness. He was fitted with everything in a tailor shop where the entire Jewish family came from a room at the back to witness the cries of approval from the Rebels as Horrie trotted around to each man for a paw shake and pat. They all felt the sheer joy of being associated with this exceptional animal.

*

The Rebels kept a tight watch and rein on Horrie for the sightseeing around Jerusalem, and the visit enlightened them further on the dog's feelings. He was hostile to any of the locals, including the predominant Arabs and Jews, and any other race or nationality, depending, it seemed, on their attire.

Horrie was undaunted by the numbers of locals as he strained at the leash on the wander through the Old City. He uttered an almost permanent low growl but rarely broke into a bark, and his antics brought reaction from the locals. Some people pointed and laughed; others backed away or sidestepped his thrusts in their direction. One brave young man bent down to pat Horrie, despite his hostility and bared fangs. The man pushed his wrist at the dog, who sniffed it. Seeing the Arab's courage and confidence, Moody said in his most conciliatory tone: 'It's okay, Horrie, mate.'

With that, Horrie relented and licked the man's wrist. His tail wagged, just. It was an *oh, all right, if you say so* reaction. Horrie would reserve judgement.

'I can be your guide, *troopers,*' the man said with a big grin. 'My name is Mohammed. I am the son of a trooper from the Great War, Sandy McKenzie.'

'Oh, are you now?' Shegog said. 'And how old would you be, *son of Sandy McKenzie*?'

'You know him, my father?' Mohammed asked.

'Of course we do,' Fitzsimmons said, 'everyone does.'

Mohammed's eyes flicked to each of the Rebels.

'I know you joke with me, but I *am* his son.'

'How old are you, mate?' Gill asked, repeating Shegog's question.

'I have 21 years,' Mohammed said.

'Born in what month and year?'

'August 3 of 1919.'

Gill pulled a half-believing face.

'Your mother met Sandy McKenzie during the war here, right?'

'No, just after the Armistice of 31 October of 1918.'

'Hmmm,' Gill muttered, 'could well be right. That all adds up. I reckon he can be our guide.'

The delighted, laughing Mohammed led them to the Wailing Wall, the best-known Jewish shrine in Jerusalem.

'Built by King Solomon in 1000 BC,' Mohammed informed them.

'I was told 1001 BC,' Fitzsimmons said with a frown as they watched worshippers bend low and kiss the ground in front of the Wall, and then the Wall itself.

'You mock me!' Mohammed said.

'I think he *really* is the son of a trooper,' Fitzsimmons said to the others, 'he doesn't miss a beat.'

'And Horrie approves of him,' Moody said with a wink to Mohammed.

He next directed them to the Old City's labyrinth-like maze of narrow streets encaged as arcades lined with endless shops. The group lingered at jewellers' shops and watched the deft work of cutting, polishing and engraving. Moody was preoccupied with the sound of people attempting to bargain over stall items. It created a cacophonous high pitch lifting from the many retail places that sold a variety of goods wrought from copper and brass to gold and silver. Intermittently for a few seconds, a Chopin polonaise could be heard coming from a gramophone record in a tiny office at the back of the shop.

'I love a good haggle,' Moody whispered to Gill and then began bartering with a jeweller over the price of a pendant he wished to be crafted from a small piece of marble he had taken from a cave at Ikingi.

'Who's that for?' Gill asked.

'Me.'

The jeweller held the marble up to the dim light shafting through roof-slits. He said he would create the pendant for no cost if he could keep the rest of the marble. Moody agreed but at that moment let Horrie's leash slip in the shop. The dog darted off with Moody and Gill in pursuit, baulking past locals, donkeys and a long line of Christian worshippers and pilgrims who were following a priest with a wooden cross on his back. The chubby priest was re-enacting the crucifixion of Christ.

'God! Where is that little four-legged bleeder?!' Moody exclaimed as they stopped to catch their breath outside St Mary's, one of several Christian churches.

'Don't think God can help us right now,' Gill said, eyeing the surging crowd of mainly women in black outside the church. 'He's a little preoccupied with pilgrims.'

'Food stalls!' Moody said, snapping his fingers. 'Butchers!'

They hurried to the main food arcade and a large butcher's shop. Horrie was there fighting hundreds of flies that were vying for the bone a Jewish butcher had given him.

'Such a nice little doggie!' the butcher said, in a northern English accent.

'When he's asleep,' Moody said, rolling his eyes. 'He loves all butchers. Makes them his new best cobber wherever he is.' He picked up the leash and led Horrie, bone in mouth, back to find Mohammed and the others at the jeweller's shop.

*

Later, on the return from Jerusalem, the Rebels enjoyed exploring the camp area, especially the ruins of the ancient city of Ascalon. Moody, as ever, took photographs and notes, and referred to a guidebook: *Ancient Palestine: Lost Tribes and Civilisations* by Angus Trollope. He tried to enthuse the others by reading passages, including reference to the Crusaders fighting many battles in and around Ascalon, and that during one in about 1170 BC, the city was destroyed.

To his surprise, Shegog commented: 'Yeah, King Herod the Great was born there.'

'Where'd that come from?' Featherstone asked in surprise.

'The Gogg's family knew the Herods well,' Fitzsimmons chimed in, 'even when they weren't so great.'

'Yes and his dad played for the Ascalon thirds,' Featherstone said.

They also explored Gaza and swam at a nearby beach. Horrie kept guard over their clothes, watches, cameras and wallets. He had a torrid time defending the pile from some local lads, who were intrepid enough to attempt to steal items by circling him and moving in. But Horrie was equal to the task that exhausted him over more than an hour's 'defence' under a boiling sun. When the Rebels had finished their swim, Moody and Gill took him into the water to help him cool down and later at camp erected a shelter for him to stay out of the heat, which he appreciated. He always had his tongue out in the conditions but never showed signs of stress.

Jerusalem became a favourite haunt and the Rebels stayed at the ancient and famous Fast's Hotel, which in World War I had been used by General Harry Chauvel when he used it as a decoy to make it appear as if the British Expeditionary Force would have its HQ there. In 1941 it had been taken over by the Comforts Fund and then transformed into the Australian Soldiers' Club. The rooms were cheap and the management allowed Horrie to stay, which enticed the Rebels to make several visits.

When they returned to Dier Suneid after one of their sojourns in Jerusalem they were greeted with the news they would be breaking camp again, this time relocating about 15 kilometres north to Khassa near El Majdal, still in Palestine.

'Why do they move us about so much?' a disgruntled Featherstone asked Brooker.

'Because they don't want you pampered lads getting too cosy,' Brooker replied, 'or building up too many possessions, like the travel books that Moods buys everywhere; or The Gogg's collection of whisky bottles and those paintings when he has them framed.'

'Gosh, Sarg, you've deeply disappointed me,' Fitzsimmons said. 'There I was believing that our moves were all part of some grand strategic plan by Churchill and Tom Blamey!'

'Nope,' Featherstone said, 'I'm beginning to think we are the forgotten battalion, or at least the invisible one; stuck out here in the flaming desert doing bugger all but playing Rugby and hockey.'

'Yeah, but we nearly always win,' Fitzsimmons replied. 'And look at the surf-lifesaving team. It won four events in a row at the Gaza Surf Carnival.'

This was to be their first move since Murchison broke away from the group and it caused another discussion about him. Horrie was alerted at the mention of his name.

'Wonder what's happened to him?' Shegog asked Brooker as they packed up. 'We haven't heard a peep. You don't think he bought the farm, do you?'

'It is a bit of a worry,' Brooker admitted for the first time.

Censorship on the Syrian campaign left the Rebels in the dark. It was months before they heard unconfirmed whispers that he may have survived the torrid battles in Syria. Rumours suggested it was possible that he remained in Syria with the 2/3 Gunners as part of the occupation force. But no one could check the truth because not even Gunner officers knew any details about individuals on the front-line in the Syrian campaign. They could only guess how long the occupation would last. The Rebels calculated that if Murchison had survived, he would have stayed on with the Australian 7th Division in the hope of more action. The Rebels realised he wouldn't fancy the prospects of even less action with his former battalion that had seemed to have done its dash in North Africa, Greece and Crete. This scenario was what they all hoped and prayed for. But they had no real idea of his fate. Although he was a careless communicator who was too lazy to write much home to relatives, they believed that if he were alive, he would get word to them. But they had not even received his speciality of a scribbled postcard. Yet if he had written anything it would not have squeezed passed the censors. Any description or mention of the Allied Syria–Lebanon campaign was suppressed. Press reporting was limited because some Allied commanders and politicians believed that knowledge about the Allies fighting the French could have a negative impact on public opinion, especially after the huge effort and sacrifice of Allied countries including the UK, Canada, Australia and most British Commonwealth countries, made on behalf of the French in World War I.

Murchison's circumstances remained unknown.

18

LOVE—DOGGIE-STYLE

Moody was surprised to find that there was another white Egyptian terrier mascot in the 2nd AIF, whose experiences almost mirrored Horrie's. It was female, a fraction taller with a full tail, which allowed the discerning onlooker to distinguish between her and Horrie. Her name was Imshi, which meant 'buzz off' in Arabic, and was so named in a typical cynical Australian manner by members of the 2/1 Anti-Tank Regiment, which was stationed at Khassa. Her master was gangling and moustachioed Bruce ('Mac') McKellary, a friend of Moody. She had also been picked up in Egypt and had toured Greece and Syria with the regiment. The two dogs of the same breed got on well, perhaps too well for the army's liking. Horrie was most stimulated by Imshi, who appealed to him far more than the sweet but timid Horrietta on Crete. Despite his worrying nine-day disappearance from the last camp, Moody, Gill and the other Rebels felt it was wiser to let him roam free, and trust that his judgement might be better after the last time. But a problem developed with the two love-dogs bounding off into the desert, sometimes all night. There was concern about Horrie's dereliction of his tent-minding and other duties, such as leading marches. He would rather spend time with Imshi.

'What the hell do they do out there in the dark all night?' Shegog asked.

'Horrie reckons they hunt lizards,' Fitzsimmons replied, 'but can you believe him?'

The Rebels and the Anti-Tank diggers became increasingly displeased. Their tents were not being guarded. A rifle went missing from the Rebels' tent when they were away one night. Normally the firing bolt would be removed, but the Rebels had been so sure of Horrie's defence of the tent that they had never bothered to hide the bolt. Until now, the Rebels were the envy of the entire battalion. All other units had to have a man on duty all day and night to ensure resourceful local Arabs, who were skilled at avoiding guards around the camp, did not take their rifles. Horrie's AWL activities changed all that. Brooker decided it had to stop. Horrie was chained to the tent pole, a predicament even he could not extricate himself from. But every morning when let loose he would seek out Imshi and they would scamper off into distant dunes until their white coats could not be distinguished from the sunlight on the sand, and they might not return until noon or even later. They built a strong bond, which was even tighter than that which they had with their respective units. The partnership was only broken two months later when the Anti-Tank Regiment was transferred to Syria. Horrie was in a most despondent state when he bounded one morning over to the former site of the regiment only to find it had gone. Moody tried to distract him by playing a mouth organ he had received as a present from home. A few of the Rebels protested at Moody's enthusiastic yet amateur effort.

'Can you play "Far, Far Away"?' Fitzsimmons asked with a frown.

'I'll give it a go,' Moody responded as he tried to remember the tune.

'Well, it's that-away,' Fitzsimmons said, pointing out of the tent to the horizon of sand.

For a while, Horrie looked to the sky and howled and wagged his tail in time to Moody's modest performance. But once the Rebels' applause had completed, and the novelty of unmelodic playing and singing had worn off, Horrie slinked off to the former Anti-Tank Regiment site again to see if his friend had reappeared. He only became distracted from his woes for a short time the next day when Moody was tuning in a radio outside the tent. Horrie was curious. Instead of wandering by like a lost soul he sat close to the earphones in much the same manner he did when Stukas were coming, and his ears stood high in his attempt to locate the source. A voice speaking Arabic emanated from the earphones. Horrie frowned, tilted his head and sniffed them. Unconvinced the owner of the voice could be squeezed into such small devices, Horrie scurried around inside and outside the tent growling in every corner and peering under beds.

'He's looking for wogs,' Gill whispered in a barely suppressed chortle. 'Better calm him down.'

Moody switched off the radio. With that, Horrie waddled out of the tent and continued on his downcast meanderings. This apparent 'depression' went on for days as he maintained his pining for his lovely companion. Just as the 'H' word was not to be used on Crete, the 'I' word was now forbidden in Palestine. But every now and again her name came up and Horrie would wag his tail in furious anticipation of a reunion. Then early in September 1941, he went missing again and the Rebels concluded that he was looking for Imshi. For a second time, they embarked on searches in the immediate area, and then the region. Five days later, some members of the battalion were travelling back from Palestine one evening when they came across Horrie limping towards Jerusalem. He had come 80 kilometres and this time his condition suggested to the Rebels he had not slipped onto a bus. His paws were in a bad state and once more he had lost weight. Yet the experience seemed to have convinced him that there was no use searching for his lost love any more. He stayed close to camp and did not stray again and Moody and Gill did their best not to leave him alone for too long. But he was not the only soul saddened over a broken relationship.

Moody himself received a 'Dear John' letter from his wife, the term used for the all-too-common occurrence of a woman waiting too long for a soldier to return from war, and becoming involved with someone else.

His six-year marriage was over. His wife wanted a divorce. Moody was not devastated. His relationship had been rocky. Yet it left him dispirited and added to a sense of helplessness and uncertainty about his future. His mates did what they could to lift his spirits. Fitzsimmons told him about a fellow gunner who had written his wife a 'Dear Jane' letter in which he had decided to divorce her because he'd fallen in love with a Greek girl he planned to marry after the war. Moody appreciated the support but it was not enough to salve his feelings. Gill decided to attempt to go one better. He had just met a short, plump Adelaide nurse, Louise Swift, working at the British Servicemen's Hospital in Jerusalem. According to Gill, she had a stunning, tall 'flame-haired' friend from Fremantle, Bonnie Maitland.

'I fancy Bonnie myself,' he told an uninterested Moody, 'but I want you to meet her. Believe me, she will take your mind off your wife.'

It took days of cajolery before Moody agreed to meet Maitland on a blind date on the condition that they could bring Horrie. The women agreed. The two Rebel privates took them by bus on a day's outing to Jaffa and an overnight stay at Haifa. Horrie was scolded for growling at Arabs in bus seats nearby. The locals looked uncomfortable. They were not used to such a coddled little aggressor.

'What a lovely little doggie you are,' Bonnie said, having heard of his now legendary heroics, 'and a lance corporal as well!' She saluted then bent across Moody to pat him. Horrie snarled and bared his teeth. Bonnie sat back in her seat.

'*Not* such a nice little doggie,' she said, startled.

'Sorry about that,' Moody apologised, 'but he is a little nervous with all the . . . er "locals" on the bus.'

'Also we think he dislikes your clothes,' Gill said from his seat next to Louise behind them.

'Oh, he's fashion conscious, is he?' Bonnie asked.

'No, I meant your civvies. He just will not accept anyone who is not in Australian uniform. He is a fair dinkum digger's dog.'

'He's not a misogynist is he?'

'I don't think so,' Gill said and asked, 'What's that?'

'A male who hates women.'

'Oh, good God no! He had a girlfriend who he was most gracious and polite and attentive with—'

The women laughed at Gill's earnest defence of Horrie. But they kept a discreet distance from the dog on the rest of the outing. His behaviour became a point of contention when the two couples booked rooms at a hotel. Horrie had to remain with Moody, who had to convince Bonnie that he would behave in the bedroom.

'As you will do,' she said with mischievous smile.

When they approached the front desk of the Hotel Sea View, the overweight Arab proprietor eyed the women.

His aquiline nose bent when he asked the men in halting English, 'I think you require a room "without," yes?'

'No, no definitely "with,"' Moody replied, assuming he was speaking about a bath.

'"With"?' the Arab said, surprised. His eyes flicked to Gill and the women and then back to Moody. Then a knowing smile creased his tanned, wrinkled features. The men nodded and were distracted by Horrie, who jumped at the counter, unhappy with the Arab. They calmed him down, and apologised a second time in the day for his 'ungracious' demeanour.

'Do not be troubled,' the proprietor said, 'but I charge you extra for dog too.'

The hotel had been recommended by other diggers lucky enough to make 'romantic' ventures to the picturesque coastal town. The second-floor rooms were spare yet spacious with superb views of the water and coastline. Moody and Bonnie were disappointed to find there was no bath, just a large wash-basin, with a small tub next to it.

'I'm sure he asked if I wanted a room "with,"' Moody said, puzzled.

'He did, I heard him,' Bonnie said. 'Mind you, his English was so poor . . .'

They shrugged off the apparent misunderstanding. Moody made Horrie comfortable on a little makeshift bed of cushions and pillows in one corner. He tried to jump on their bed, but was admonished and gave up with an ill-mannered growl at Bonnie. After lights out Moody whispered that they should wait until Horrie had dropped off to sleep. A few minutes after the light was switched off, they heard the dog's familiar low whistle punctuated by short, uneven grunts.

'He's dreaming,' Moody whispered.

'Aw, so cute, when he's asleep,' Bonnie said.

Just as they embraced there was a soft knock at the door. Horrie leapt off his bed and barked. Moody pulled on trousers and ordered Horrie to 'back off!' He opened the door and popped his head out. A beautiful, brown-eyed Arab girl of about 20, wearing a bright red-and-green floral summer dress and no shoes, had already retreated down the passageway.

'Yes?' Moody said.

The girl hesitated.

'You wanted a girl, no?' she enquired in a French-tinged accent.

'Well, no, I have—'

Horrie barked again, breaking Moody's concentration. Then it struck him. The proprietor's question about 'with' or 'without' was in reference to a *prostitute.* After a garbled explanation to Bonnie, Moody hastened downstairs to rectify the matter with the proprietor. Moody restrained himself from explaining to the bemused Arab that this misunderstanding may have ruined his evening, just as Gill came down with the same complaint about another young woman at his door. The discussion heated up and the flustered proprietor asked: 'Not without, no?'

'No,' Gill said, 'we have women with us!'

'Not without, no?' the proprietor repeated.

'No, sport,' Gill said, raising his voice, 'we have two women with us. We don't need four!'

'Okay, okay, okay,' the proprietor said in an understanding tone. 'Arh! Very good, very good.' He grinned. 'You Aussie!'

'Yeah,' Moody said with a relieved grin, 'we Aussies are not greedy!'

The proprietor laughed. 'No, no, you Aussie not greedy!' He waved his hands flamboyantly. 'It is good for business.'

The two men were puzzled but returned to their rooms. Moody was shocked to find Horrie had cornered Bonnie on the bed. She was standing on the pillows, her hands up as if the little dog had a gun. He was on his hind legs, front paws on the bed, and snarling as if ready to jump up at her. Moody gave him a slap on the behind and placed him back in his corner. Moody had some explaining to do to the distressed Bonnie. She got down from the bed, sat in a chair, then folded her arms and crossed her legs, while keeping a nervous eye on the still-growling Horrie, who stared at her. Louise came to the door and asked if she could speak with Bonnie in private. They chatted in the corridor and then put an ultimatum to the men: either they slept together in one room without the men and Horrie, or the men had to take them by bus back to Jerusalem. It was after midnight. The men agreed to sleep in one room: Moody on a couch, Gill in the bed and Horrie still in his corner. The two women took the other room and locked the door.

Not a half-hour later, there were knocks on both doors. The proprietor had directed four prostitutes to visit Moody and Gill. Again, Horrie made a ruckus. The men dismissed the prostitutes and again confronted the proprietor, who had for a second time misunderstood their conversation. But the damage was done. Bonnie and Louise assumed the men had ordered the sex workers, and they were furious. No amount of explanation was accepted and the night ended in a frosty gender divide with no appeasement at breakfast the next morning. The women sat together on the bus, well away from Horrie and the men, and hardly addressed them on the journey back to their Jerusalem hospital. The four parted with perfunctory handshakes, but not before Bonnie had looked down at Horrie, who eyed her with distrust.

'You *are* a misogynist,' she said to him with an accusing point of her finger, 'and I know where you learnt it from!'

The two men and Horrie were left feeling glum and misunderstood. Moody was despondent, admitting that Bonnie had indeed taken his mind off his wife. But his failure to capitalise on the opportunity with her depressed him further. They sauntered a little way down the street from the bus depot and found a cafe. They ordered beer, and milk for Horrie, and sat in silence, Gill rolling a cigarette and Moody filling his pipe, while watching people getting on and off buses. Quite a few diggers were among them. One large digger alighted and seemed to be in some push-and-shove with a group of unhappy Arabs. Moody and Gill stood, ready to go to his aid. But the digger, whose considerable girth matched his height, seemed unconcerned by his tormentors. He staggered to their cafe, with about six Arabs following him, hurling abuse and gesticulating. The big man sank down into a chair on the sidewalk near them. He rubbed his large nose that was gnarled and askew from perhaps another hostile encounter at another time.

'You all right, Dig?' Moody said, still standing.

'Yeah, Dig,' he mumbled, clearly inebriated, 'abused a bus full of wogs. Do it all the time. Shouldn't, I know, but I couldn't give a fuck! They're all bloody bastards!'

Moody and Gill resumed their seats but were disturbed by the indignant Arabs, who seemed to be cursing the digger. One held a knife. Moody noticed blood on the digger's army shirt, which was slashed.

'What's your name, mate?' Moody said, staying cool in the tense atmosphere.

'Ray Wallace,' the big man said, shaking hands with them.

'Better have that cleaned up,' Moody said, indicating the seven centimetre cut on his right arm. 'There's a hospital just down the road . . .'

'Nar, Dig; it's just a nick.'

'Did one of them do it to you?' Gill asked as he also noticed the Arab with the knife.

'Yeah, that prick there,' Wallace said. He was having trouble focusing as he nodded towards the thin man with the weapon. Horrie started seething at the Arabs. He barked and jumped forward. Moody restrained him.

'You!' Wallace said, reaching for Horrie. 'I know who you are! You are a fuckin' legend! A fuck-ing legend!!'

'How'd you know about his sex-life?' Moody quipped.

'Hey?' Wallace asked, not quite understanding the joke, but laughing anyway. He eyed Horrie and added, 'You're with the 2/1 Gunners. You've saved about a million lives, I hear . . .' Wallace's sudden switch to a friendly demeanour had Horrie change his mood also in an instant. Wallace picked Horrie up and cuddled him. The dog licked his face, sniffed his cut arm and licked the congealed blood on that too. Two of the Arabs moved a few seats closer. Horrie struggled to get free. His fur was up, his eyes demonic.

'Don't come any closer,' Wallace yelled, 'you wog bastards!'

The Arabs, all fit-looking and in their early twenties, hurled abuse back.

'This has been going on all the way from bloody . . .' Wallace began, and then frowned in a struggle to recall the town, 'I dunno . . . Arar . . . bloody rat . . . I dunno . . .'

'You've certainly riled them,' Gill said, making eye contact with Moody. Both were concerned there could be real trouble any moment. They tried to placate the big man.

'I told 'em what I thought of them,' Wallace said, turning to curse them again, 'but they don't get it . . . they don't know what rat-infested . . .'

'Now, Dig,' Moody said, 'hadn't you better lay off? Who's your unit?'

'My unit? What do you want to know my unit for?'

'Just want to get you home in one piece, Dig, that's all,' Gill said.

'I know yours . . .. you're the 2/1 Gunners. I know because of the colour patch and the dog.' He looked down at Horrie again and grinned. Horrie forgot about the Arabs for a second and wagged his behind and tail. Wallace looked into the cafe and waved a heavy hand at the owner, who seemed reluctant to come out to the sidewalk. 'What's a bloke gotta do to get a beer around here?'

'Where are you based, Dig?'

'Somewhere out there in the desert,' he slurred, then turned to hurl more vitriol at the Arabs in Arabic, which in translation was roughly *sons of whores and bitches.* This ranked high in the list of local insults, and only a rung or two below insulting Mohammed. It guaranteed the recipients would return verbal fire and even something more life-threatening.

'Better to lay off that language, Ray, mate,' Moody said in a placatory tone, 'only going to cause trouble.'

'No, bugger it! Bugger them!! We come here in the last war and an uncle of mine had his throat cut in the night by a gutless wog! He was bloodiwell asleep and one of these bastards' relatives did it!'

'I am sorry to hear that, mate, I really am. But this is another war, another time,' Moody said. 'They see us as invaders of their land—'

'You see, Dig,' Gill added, 'what if they invaded Australia and camped in our desert, even if they were on their way to fight someone else? We wouldn't like it.'

'What? We wouldn't let these arseholes in our country, mate— never!'

'Sort of makes my point,' Gill said with a short, nervous laugh, but he did not 'debate' any further. Wallace was too drunk for any rational discussion.

The Arab with the knife stood only a few paces from Wallace. Seeing this, the big man lurched at the Arab, but was soon set upon by the other five who brought him down in a crash of tables and chairs. Gill moved in, throwing punches. Moody let Horrie go and joined in. Wallace was being kicked as he lay on the ground. Horrie flew at one of the Arabs, biting his ankle. The Arab with the knife straddled Wallace and was angling to drive the curved weapon into his heart, when Moody brought a wooden chair down so hard on his head and back that the chair legs broke off. The Arab fell unconscious on top of Wallace, his knife inflicting a wound in Wallace's shoulder. Just at that moment, several diggers alighted from a bus. Seeing fellow Australians in a brawl, they all hurried to the cafe, causing the remaining Arabs to make a quick departure, one with a decided limp from Horrie's attack. They rushed down a lane next to the cafe, with Horrie in hot pursuit. Moody chased after him, ordering him to 'Come here or else!' The dog stopped and turned back.

The other Australian soldiers helped Wallace to his feet. He was now bleeding from the two cuts.

'Better take you down to the hospital,' Moody said. He looked at the Arab he had struck. He was lying face down in a crumpled position and had not moved since the incident. 'Better take him too.'

'No, leave the bastard!' Wallace shouted. 'He tried to kill me!'

Gill turned the Arab over. He retrieved a bucket of water from the cowering owner, and threw it flush into the stricken Arab's face. His eyes blinked; his mouth twitched. Gill asked two soldiers to help him carry the Arab, while two others assisted Wallace on a straggling march 200 metres to the hospital. By chance, Bonnie and Louise were the two nurses on duty in Emergency. They were cool and efficient, and barely acknowledged Moody and Gill.

'What happened to you?' Bonnie said, examining Wallace's shoulder and arm.

He began to answer by pointing at the Arab stretched out on the floor, but Moody cut him off and said: 'He was at the circus, and accidentally stumbled in front of a knife-throwing act.'

Bonnie gave Moody a withering look, her pen poised over a patient report sheet.

'And him?' she asked, nodding to the prostrate Arab, 'I suppose he ran into a door?'

'No,' Gill said, 'a chair.'

Wallace laughed, and mumbled a 'thank you' to Moody.

'Do the same for a white fella,' Moody said.

'Nar, I owe you one, mate!' Wallace slurred. 'I may be shicka, but I know what happened. Boy! That chair . . . !'

Louise had called for an English doctor to examine the Arab, who had stirred. He tried to sit up. The doctor was used to dealing with countless results of fights among servicemen. He examined him, shining a small torch into his eyeballs, and looking at the egg-sized bump on the back of his head and the graze on his back.

'Concussion,' the doctor said, pointing to the report sheet in Bonnie's hand. 'Keep him in a room overnight. Release him in the morning.' He turned to Wallace, looked at his arm and shoulder, and said, 'They'll need stitches now before the flies get into them.'

'They already have,' Wallace sneered with contempt at the Arab, who, although dazed, looked frightened when he focused on Wallace.

'Let it be, mate,' Moody said to Wallace, 'let it be.'

19
SYRIAN ODYSSEY

The Nazi attack on Russia in mid-1941 had rapid and early successes but, as the months slipped by, there was less certainty about the outcome. The Russians had not given way under the onslaught, which meant there was not quite the urgency about the 6th Division's position in Syria after they had defeated the Vichy French. The expected Nazi thrust south at Middle East oilfields and the Suez Canal had not come. But still, the division was needed to help form a line of defence across Syria. In conjunction with this in early October, the 2/1 Machine Gun Battalion began to receive eagerly awaited Vickers guns since most of their weapons had been lost in Greece and Crete. By early in November 1941 the battalion learned it was due to move north to Syria later in the month, yet not to meet any new Nazi push.

In anticipation of a severe winter there, the Rebels fashioned a miniature coat for Horrie out of a discarded coat belonging to Featherstone, who had been promoted to corporal. They lined the edges with white tape. Brass buttons and two stripes were retained.

'That's a small consolation for losing I—' Featherstone began to say when Horrie modelled his new gear for the Rebels. Even the utterance of the first letter had Horrie on alert.

'Independence!' Moody said with a frown and then a smile at Horrie. 'You won't be able to run so freely in the snow in Syria!'

*

Snow was falling on the top of distant Lebanese mountains when the Rebels' truck convoy approached the small Lebanese village of Zaboude near the battalion base at Ras Baalbek, 1100 metres above sea level. Horrie was at a window on his hind legs, observing everything of this new territory. There were fewer people to see in fewer villages but his interest did not wane. He just remained quiet, his tail still. As usual, Moody had a guidebook. Despite the derision of the others, he began to recite passages. They were attentive for a moment or two before the inevitable descent into frivolity.

He began by informing them that the local ruins provided evidence that Ras Baalbek existed as a Greek

City: Heliopolis. The guidebook suggested that it became a Roman colony in about 554 AD and that the Great Temple was destroyed by lightning and fire. It further claimed that after the disaster it had become a centre of Pagan worship. Muslims centuries later formed the Acropolis of Ras Baalbeck into a fortress.

'Oooh, pagan worship, eh?' Shegog said, emptying yet another whisky flask. 'We'd better be careful.'

'What I don't understand is why everything has to be so *old*,' Featherstone interjected. 'Why can't they have a few new towns like Perth or Yallourn? Why do we have to look at crumbled old buildings all the time? What about a few modern structures that stay upright, like in New York?'

'It's good to see there are still one or two Philistines in the area,' Fitzsimmons said.

The convoy rumbled along the valley. The air became nippy and soon it was cold. Horrie's demeanour changed. This was an unfamiliar land without shimmering, flat desert spotted with sand dunes. He seemed fascinated by what he saw but the freezing atmosphere upset him. He stopped looking out the window and soon bundled up in a ball in Moody's lap. Not even his greatcoat would be enough for these conditions.

At the new camp, keeping warm became the first priority for everyone, including Horrie. He was a desert dog and he struggled to combat the freezing conditions. It was a battle for him, even inside the specially designed Nissen huts, with their pegged wire supports to prevent them from being blown away in the howling mountain winds, and their sloping round roofs to cause the predicted snow to roll off. On the third morning Horrie grabbed one of Featherstone's socks in front of him and took off outside into the snow. This act was not appreciated by the fastidious corporal. Whereas the other Rebels barely complied with dress codes, Featherstone, who declared himself 'my own batman,' always looked neatly pressed, with his boots shiny, his hair combed and even his socks ironed. For one sock to be taken in such a wanton, unprovoked manner by the tiniest battalion member was irritating. Featherstone followed Horrie, demanding his sock back. The dog let him get close and then darted off, much to the mirth of the others. They, too, joined in the chase but could not catch the nibble Horrie, who toyed with them, sock in mouth and tail wagging. Soon all the Rebels surrounded him, but he avoided their cumbersome efforts to nab him in the slippery conditions. The eel-like dog just could not be caught. Twenty minutes into the game, his tongue was hanging out in fatigue, but he kept going until all the Rebels gave up, puffing and in urgent need of a cigarette or pipe. Horrie then dropped the saliva-stained item at Featherstone's feet.

'He has always had fun with socks, but this was a far more sustained game than anything he did before,' Featherstone observed, as he began to clean his chewed sock. 'I wonder why.'

'I reckon he did it to warm up,' Gill said, to much derision from the others, but then on reflection, some agreed that it was an odd game for him to start playing on his own volition, especially as he had never done it before with such dedicated vigour. All observed him lying by a stove, still panting from his efforts. When he repeated variants of the act each morning, usually with Featherstone's socks, all agreed that the aim was to get blood running through his long body and stunted legs.

'You know,' Brooker said one night at battalion mess, 'I worry a little about what is going to become of the pup after this show is over. We picked him up when he was just a few months old. Now he's nearly a year, and the way he behaves, we are all family to him, with Moods and Gillie, as, if you like, his two "parents."'

'Like all good relatives, we must get him home,' Shegog said, looking at Moody, whose expression remained non-committal. 'He's a fair dinkum Aussie dog now, as sure as if he came out of our outback. He knows how to take a joke—'

'As long as he is not ridiculed,' Fitzsimmons interjected.

'Yeah,' Shegog went on, 'but he knows how to play a joke, fool around . . .'

'Drink at the bar,' Fitzsimmons said, '—well, milk anyway. And don't forget the girls. He likes female company.'

'Speaking of which,' Brooker said, 'I hear the Anti-Tank Regiment is due to join the camp in about a week . . .'

*

At the end of the first week at Zaboude, Horrie succumbed to the cold and he appeared to come down with a canine influenza. Moody and Gill fussed about him, wrapping him in blankets and old pullovers. Featherstone warmed rocks on the fire and put them in his basket-bed under a makeshift mini-mattress. A doctor was summoned from the Ras Baalbeck base. He examined the forlorn little animal, whose soulful expression made it appear as if he was at death's door. The doctor kept apologising for not being a vet, which was his excuse for a non-diagnosis, but he did prescribe a special diet of warm porridge and milk. Horrie refused it unless he was spoonfed, and this task fell to each diligent and concerned Rebel in shifts. Soon he became so listless that Fitzsimmons observed: 'Perhaps we should ask the Luftwaffe to send over a squadron of Stukas to stir him.' But when none of the other Rebels even grinned, he muttered almost to himself, 'It might be time for the padre to visit.'

'Not funny, Fitz,' Brooker said with a shake of the head.

'I didn't mean for the dog. It's you blokes who need a spiritual lift. You aren't helping by being so damned mournful. You're making Horrie feel worse!'

The battalion priest did make a visit but went to great pains to say that he was not making a professional call. He claimed his role was 'to minister to human flock only, for only they can enter the kingdom of heaven.'

'We think he is an angel,' Fitzsimmons said. 'You save them, don't you?'

'I agree that he is a gift from God,' the padre remarked. 'Why else would he be found by one of the division in the middle of nowhere, only to end up saving the lives of every battalion member and others on many occasions?'

'I think we just got lucky,' Fitzsimmons said. 'We showed him kindness and took him in. He responded in his doggie way, which just happened to be salvation for us.'

'Your meeting him would not be by chance, Private.'

'With respect, Padre,' Fitzsimmons interjected again, 'if he is a gift from God, then surely he is worthy of your blessing; your prayers for his life?'

'My prayers, yes, but not my blessing,' the priest said, becoming uncomfortable. 'It is not within the province of the Church to bless animals. Only humans.'

'Then we suggest you get praying, Padre.'

'Are you Catholic, Private?' the priest asked.

'No, was. I'm lapsed. I'm agnostic. Haven't quite progressed to atheism, but I'm working on it.' Fitzsimmons paused and added, 'And you're helping.'

The priest left in a huff. Horrie's condition brought a steady stream of battalion member well-wishers. Barry the Butcher brought a fresh cut of prime beef, chopped up into tiny pieces like mincemeat. Horrie sniffed it and turned his head away. Barry shook his head and brushed away tears as he left the Rebels' hut. The word spread that Horrie was near the end. The numbers making a final visit to the one who had saved their lives in one country or another increased to the point where Brooker was forced to place a medical bulletin on the hut door twice a day. One read: 'The condition of Horrie continues to be grave. He accepted only a little warm porridge during the morning . . .'

Horrie lost weight and looked about as thin as he did after his nine-day walkabout in Palestine. He shivered, he sneezed, he dry-retched often. His shrinking body shivered whether awake or asleep. On Day 6 of what had become a deathwatch, Bruce McKellary of the Anti-Tank Regiment, which camped alongside the Gunners, knocked on the door. He carried Imshi, who was wearing a warm coat of the regiment's colours and a pink beret. She was placed on the floor and made a dash for Horrie in his basket near the stove. She licked him awake. His eyes widened for the first time in days. To the amazement of the Rebels, he stood and stretched. His legs were unsteady, but there was no mistaking his grand effort to look 'well.' Imshi found her own way over to the hut the next morning and Horrie responded to her presence. The Rebels put on his uniform and he wandered awkwardly and slowly outside to be with her. She was much more active in their playful reunion but slowly, gradually, his tail wagged and his derrière became more active. After eight days, he went to the hut door himself to meet her and they bounded off together. He even brought Imshi back at night to sleep in his own warm cot under Moody's bed.

'You don't think we were conned, do you?' Brooker asked the others.

'You're not suggesting he was acting, are you?' Shegog asked. 'I mean, he has lost a lot of weight!'

'Let's put it this way,' Brooker replied, 'there has to be an element of the malingerer in the little beggar. But who cares? He's back!'

'Yeah,' Shegog agreed, 'who cares if he wangled a lot more attention than normal? It's so great to see him so alive!'

The medical bulletin on the door on Day 9 said: 'Horrie has made a miraculous recovery. We put it down to the attractive blond nurse Imshi from our illustrious Anti-Tank Regiment. Love conquers all, even, in this instance, death. We thank you for your sympathy and concern for the Battalion hero and mascot.'

At mess that night, Brooker proposed a question for the Rebels: 'Why do you think the entire battalion has shown Horrie so much love and affection?'

The others looked at each as if the answer was obvious.

'Well?' Brooker prompted.

'He's saved just about everyone's life at some moment, hasn't he?' Gill responded.

'C'mon,' Brooker urged, 'it's much more than that, although his heroism triggers the diggers' feelings, I'll grant you that.'

No one could offer further explanation.

'I'll tell you what his popularity is also about,' Brooker added, putting down his knife and fork and pushing his plate away. 'I've been in two big wars. Men kill and maim and hate the enemy. You've all had a go at firing the Vickers and they can kill several men in seconds. Machine guns have an awesome power and such weapons do strange things to men manning them. Gunners are closer to action than artillery gunners, or air force gunners. Our boys—some of you included—have been closer to mass killings than any other members of our army. This makes hard men even harder, and I don't care what anyone says, it is not man's natural nature or mentality to be so tough, so damned brutal.' He looked around at each of them in turn before continuing: 'You and every member of this mighty battalion needs a balance to that; an antidote, if you like. Some of you will be thinking of the girls you've had from Cairo to everywhere. That is not what I'm talking about. That's just finding an outlet for your crude natural instincts. That's not about real feeling or emotion or love. But Horrie is a different proposition. He is the recipient of all that balance of positive feelings from a thousand gunners. He is of course a worthy recipient of their love and sympathy. But for what it's worth, that is my theory.'

The others went on eating without speaking for some time as they reflected on Brooker's burst of profundity.

'I know what I want to be reincarnated as,' Fitzsimmons said, breaking the silence.

They all smiled in anticipation of a 'Fitzism.'

'What?' Moody asked. 'A war dog?'

'Yes, Moods, you mind-reader! But not in a gunners' battalion. I'd prefer the nurses' contingent.'

20

ENTER JAPAN

Horrie was well enough to accompany Moody and Gill on a hunting trip a few days later on 8 December in the Lebanese mountains, although the men were not quite sure about what their prey would be. There was talk from the locals about wild animals such as wolves, foxes and gazelles, but for most the expedition was more in hope than expectation. They were led by a local 17-year-old Syrian guide, whose family they would stay with. In the first hours of the trek the most exciting discovery was an old broken Vichy French tank. Horrie explored it with his usual fervour.

The little hunting party moved on up a mountain until they encountered a big wolf. It stood about ten metres away, blocking their path. Horrie bent low and took a few paces forward, protecting the two Rebels. Gill trained his rifle on the wolf, while Moody hurried to free his camera from a backpack.

'Stand fast!' Moody commanded Horrie, whose ears flicked back in recognition only. Moody managed a couple of quick snaps with Horrie in the foreground and the wolf looking on with almost a detached air. It seemed more curious than ready to flee or attack, and Horrie was his main focus. Moody stepped forward to stop Horrie, but the dog anticipated his move and made his dash at the far bigger animal, with the three humans following up. The wolf turned and bolted down the mountainside, with Horrie snapping at his heels. They raced through bushes, sidestepping boulders and rocks. Moody and Gill were yelling at Horrie to stop, realising that if the wolf made a stand, Horrie would be killed. But the wolf's flight pumped up Horrie's courage and he took a dive at the wolf's foot. He latched onto it. But that was enough for the wolf. He stopped and swung his jaws down to grip Horrie by the neck and shake him, just as the others tumbled into the two animals. The wolf's hold was broken and he ran off. This time Moody was quicker. He grabbed Horrie. Gill fired a warning shot in the air and the wolf was soon out of sight. But Horrie was ready to make hot pursuit. He knew he would catch the scent and while his neck was studded with teeth marks, he was ready to fight to the death. Moody hung on for another half-hour as the fearless little terrier showed that somewhere in his genetic make-up he was a real hunter, perhaps in packs after bigger animals such as wolves or even lions in the Libyan desert.

They stayed overnight at the mountain home of the young guide and then returned down the mountain and back to battalion base and news that would affect all of them. On 7 December 1941, the Japanese had attacked the American territory of Pearl Harbor, in Hawaii, which extended war into the Pacific and changed the entire dynamic of the global conflict. Even more alarming for the Australians were Japan's concurrent concerted strikes on Thailand, Malaya and Singapore. The 2nd AIF's 8th Division of 27,000 diggers stationed in Singapore was now under threat.

Everyone at Zaboude agreed that it could spell the end of the 6th Division's fighting in the Middle East. The Japanese attacks in the Pacific and closer to home in South-East Asia made this a near certainty. Yet no new directives arrived before Christmas. Snow fell and made life more difficult for all the men. Horrie was too low to the ground to walk through the snow and had to make the effort to bound and leap everywhere. If the Rebels were detailed to chip ice off the road or shovel snow away, Horrie would be at hand to guard their equipment and clothes and more than earned his way with hard running while carrying wireless messages in a leather tobacco-pouch from the Signals office to HQ. He was also a help in passing telephone lines through culverts under a road. The line would be attached to his collar. One Rebel would hold him at the culvert's entrance. Moody would call him from the other end. No matter how claustrophobic or tiny the culvert, Horrie would run, slide or crawl through it and be pleased with his own efforts when rewarded with a pat, a compliment or even a biscuit. He was more effective than a mountain goat charging down mountains and hills with lines again attached. His popularity reached new heights when he couriered London Reuter's news, translated from Morse code courtesy of Harlor's modified wireless, to groups of gunners in different areas of the camp.

Moody used all his dog-teaching experience to instruct Horrie, but it usually only took one lesson. He had always believed Rudyard, a red setter he had trained in Australia, was the smartest animal he had ever encountered. But now after a year with Horrie under tutelage, he was beginning to change his mind.

'He is so quick on the uptake,' Moody told the others one day on the road during a smoko break, 'and when you combine it with his courage and risk-taking, it now puts him out in front of any creature I've ever experienced. He is prepared to do anything you ask, if he trusts you. And he trusts every single one of us.'

'You mean every damned digger,' Fitzsimmons observed, 'as long as he has on at least army issue underwear.'

*

The mood in the camp changed further when Harlor's 'special' radio picked up the shocking news that on 10 December 1941 the Japanese had sunk the two large British battleships, *The Prince of Wales* and *Repulse*, which had been sent by the British Prime Minister, Winston Churchill, to bolster Singapore. It was a huge blow to the Allied cause and a fright for Australia, which was looking vulnerable and unprotected. Three of its four combat divisions were in the Middle East and a long way from home, while the fourth (8th Division) was in Singapore and about to face the Japanese onslaught in Malaya. Americans were slipping into Brisbane and Melbourne over the New Year, but they were not combat troops. Should the Japanese decide to attack Australia, they would find little resistance. This situation began to create frustration among the gunners in Syria. By late in January 1942, and with the knowledge that the battalion would be moving soon, each man became disgruntled over the conditions. The beauty of the snow settled on the mountains and their village like a white crocheted blanket was less and less compensation for these diggers for being so isolated and far away from any action. This was especially as their own country was now in danger from marauding Japanese forces who were every day slicing their way through Malaya en route to Singapore. Daily reports via Harlor's radio told of countries falling like dominoes to the Japanese in South-East Asia and the Pacific. Doubts were mounting in BBC radio broadcasts about the alleged impregnability of the so-called island fortress of Singapore.

The weather took its toll on Horrie again after two months. The icy surface affected his feet and he was not able any more to be the diligent news messenger. Moody applied Vaseline to ease his difficulty but this did not work. As ever, the Rebels ingenuity and indulgence came to the fore to assist. Shegog and Featherstone fashioned a wooden sledge with a rope attached, and each member took it in turns to ferry him to various locations so he would stay with the Rebels and remain on duty. But his courier days were over in this frozen region.

*

Just at the point where some of the men were talking about going AWL south to sunnier climes in Palestine, the order came to move out. There was no official word on immediate or ultimate destinations but speculation among the diggers mounted. Bets were laid on them ending up in Singapore aiding the British army, and particularly Australia's beleaguered 8th Division, or Java, or Australia itself. The least popular possible destination was Libya again, and many diggers swore they would go permanently AWL if plonked there once more. Fitzsimmons reflected the general feeling when he remarked in a letter home to a relative: 'The word "desert" has two meanings when it comes to Libya: too much boring barren sand, and quitting the army. They are somehow fused in this instance.'

*

In early February 1942, the battalion prepared to leave. Moody took Horrie over to the Anti-Tank Regiment so he could have a final romp with Imshi.

'Who knows if they will ever meet again?' McKellary said as the two dogs ran around in a sheltered area under trees.

'Oh, I don't know,' Moody replied, 'what were the odds they would meet in the first place?'

The battalion convoy rolled out of the camp with Horrie standing on his hind legs in a truck at a window watching Imshi as they passed the regiment's camp. He kept silent until she was out of sight, then he emitted a whine of discontent. Moody patted and consoled him.

'It's okay,' he reassured him, 'you'll see Imshi again.'

But Horrie's look of agitation perhaps registered that he was not so sure. The second parting of the two put him off his food for several days but the battalion's next location was a consolation for the lovesick one-year-old. To his and every gunner's delight, a green-tinged base near Tel Aviv on the Mediterranean coast was their new temporary base. The men took time out to swim at the beach or visit the city. The Rebels visited a cinema one night. Horrie became the centre of attention for hundreds of diggers in attendance, not for alerting them to incoming Stukas, but for his antics in watching a movie. He stood on Moody's lap, put his feet on the back of the seat in front, and watched every second of the films on the program, which included a short on *Life in Palestine*, and the 1940 Charlie Chaplin feature *The Great Dictator*. Much to the amusement of all around him, he growled at every animal that appeared on the screen in the short, with dogs, cattle and horses receiving a special reception of barks. His intense viewing for two hours without intermission or a break became more entertaining to the diggers than the films themselves. He remained irritated by anyone in civvies yet he became angry at the sight of Chaplin playing Hitler, causing a huge roar of approval for his response. At least a hundred diggers crowded around Horrie at the movie's end. Moody was forced to field questions, which centred on the dog's future. What would the Rebels be doing with the battalion's mighty symbol?

'I just don't know, Dig,' became Moody's stock response. Even if he had worked out a plan, he was not about to let anyone in on it apart from fellow Rebels. On the bus ride back to camp, they discussed what should be done.

'I know one thing,' Moody remarked, 'loose lips sink ships. Once we do have a plan, we tell no one outside our group. Better still, we make up another story to throw everyone off the scent, okay?'

Everyone agreed. Gill suggested that Horrie would be given to the (British) Palestine police station or 'blockhouse' at Ascalon, a few kilometres from their camp. These three-storey square buildings were fully stocked with food and water to allow the occupants to survive for at least a year. The buildings were positioned in strategic spots through the desert. Each one had a tall observation tower that could communicate with the next one if telephone lines went down. They were there primarily to put down any possible local Arab uprisings, and had been converted into mini-fortresses during the war.

'All the police are Pommies and good blokes,' Gill said, 'and Moods and I have already had chats with them. They are pretty keen to take him on as their mascot.'

The others looked stunned.

'And what?' Featherstone asked. 'Leave him there?!'

'Yes,' Moody replied, 'for about a week.'

'Then what?'

'We want everyone to think we've given him away and that we wanted him to avoid being destroyed. The order will be given very soon that all pets be killed.'

'That way,' Gill added, 'everyone will think we've done the right thing by the dog.'

The others liked the plan.

'But how will you get him back?' Shegog asked with a frown. 'The British cops are not that stupid, are they?'

'No, not stupid at all,' Moody said.

'We'll find a way of retrieving him,' Gill said, glancing at Moody, 'just haven't come to that bit yet.'

The next morning they left Horrie with the police as planned. He became distressed when he saw Moody walking off without more than a pat and a goodbye hug. He sat, stood, circled the anteroom of the station and then began barking. It was a mixed sound of disbelief and surprise. But it also had a ring of distress. Moody found it tough to stride off to a borrowed motorbike for the drive back to camp. From then on he had to field hundreds of questions about Horrie. Some agreed that the solution was sensible and that it had saved his life. Others were disappointed, even surprised that Moody, who had managed to smuggle him through Egypt, Palestine, Greece, Crete and Syria and back to Palestine, had not devised a scheme to make the ultimate move with him back to Australia. But Moody, his bland, poker expression in play, acted the sad figure who ended each conversation by saying what a good home Horrie would have 'with the local police, who were very kind and loving to him.'

Most accepted the practicable, humane explanation, while only few expressed bitter disappointment. Just a couple of gunners were a little hostile. Barry the Butcher was so distressed that Moody had to take him aside and assure him with a nudge and a wink that everything would be okay.

'I am going down to the cop shop with some meat for him,' Barry replied, most relieved that his littlest mate, and lifesaver, was not be abandoned.

While the butcher was showing his concern and love for Horrie early that afternoon, it was announced that all pets, 'including dogs, cats, mice, snakes, monkeys, birds and any other creatures, living or otherwise, must be forfeited for destruction. The penalty for not doing so will be six months in prison in Palestine.'

It was a typical wartime order: authoritarian, cold and efficient, and with no room for compromise, debate or concession. Every gunner knew that half a year in the brig would mean missing the boat home, which would be a high price for not turning in a pet bird, or even a dog.

*

Singapore fell to the Japanese on 15 February 1942, and 23,000 members of Australia's 8th Division were taken prisoner, along with 50,000 more British troops. They were incarcerated in Changi prison. It was another huge shock for the Allies, and it shook every Australian citizen, member of the armed forces and politician. It meant that the nation was down to just three trained combat divisions—about 100,000 crack troops—but they were still out of the country and a long way away in the northern hemisphere. Prime Minister John Curtin ordered them to return, much to the chagrin of Churchill, who wanted these troops to remain in his much bigger war in Europe. Then on 19 February 1942, four days after the collapse of Singapore, the Japanese hit Darwin with 188 bombers and fighter aircraft. They flattened that city and sank 46 American and Australian ships in Darwin Harbour. The need for the nation's top combat soldiers became urgent, for many in Canberra and the 2nd AIF believed that this destruction of Darwin (and the taking of Timor a few days later) was the prelude to attacking and annexing Australia. Certainly this was the immediate aim of Japan's most successful soldier, General Yamashita, who masterminded and won Singapore for the Imperial Army using just 34,000 troops against 80,000 British combat troops. He was well supported in his thinking about securing Australia by several key Japanese admirals, who had taken control of the Pacific. Yamashita's idea was simple and logistically smart. He wanted to remove Australia as a massive 'floating aircraft carrier' for an expected backlash from the USA after the attack on its territory of Hawaii.

The sudden turn of events imperilling Australia led to a war of cables between Churchill and Curtin. This had an impact on the 7th Division, which was already heading into the Indian Ocean en route to Fremantle.

*

While these momentous events were building, the 6th Division was getting ready for its trip that would follow only a fortnight after the 7th Division, and Moody stepped up his own plans for Horrie to be with them. He began digging a hole two metres long, two metres deep and less than a metre wide under his bed. It was a long job and had to be done at night when buckets of sand would be spirited from the tent. Every Rebel pitched in and the hideaway was prepared in several nights of exertion and subterfuge. A dish of water was placed in one corner and some old clothes and a cushion in another for Horrie's maximum comfort in his blacked-out dungeon. Three thick wooden planks were placed over the hole. A cane mat, Moody's old mattress, was rolled over the planks and the bed was slid over the top of that. It was all completed with the keenness of inmates attempting to tunnel from a maximum security prison. And the stakes were higher than that for an average prison break. If Horrie was found in the hole, he would be shot.

On that fifth night, when the dog's underground room was prepared, Moody hopped on a motorbike alone and roared off to Ascalon. He parked the bike in an alley close to the blockhouse in the centre of the town and walked down a narrow lane behind it. Moody sweated in the sultry night, mindful that he was about to 'steal' something from a police station. He could hear nothing at the rear of the station behind a high stone wall where there were cells and a small yard. He whistled and stood back in the shadows. Nothing. He whistled again, and called 'Horrie' hoarsely, in a half-yell and half-whisper. Then, to Moody's surprise, he saw a white flash scuttling into the lane and charging for him. Moody picked up the writhing, yelping Horrie and dashed for his bike, and was off. He half-expected the police to come running out with their hand guns raised and giving a command to 'Stop or I'll shoot.' But there was no response at all. Part one of Plan A was complete. Part two was to deposit the dog in the hole. With all the Rebels in a circle around Moody's bed, Horrie was taught to stay in the darkness, aided by some bribing with meat purloined from the butcher. At first Horrie wagged his tail, thinking it was a new 'fun' game, but Moody's tone—reserved for serious instruction—soon told him that this was a 'command and obey' moment. He responded with all the concentration of a Buddhist monk. His eyes remained fixed on Moody, looking for any extra clues from his master's facial expression or hand movement that would help explain this 'exercise.'

There was enough air for him to survive and the hole would be less than stifling early in the day, although mid-afternoon, when the sun was at its highest point, it would be a trial for the young dog. With that 'trick' accomplished, he was allowed to sleep at Moody's feet during the night. When the Rebels went to breakfast, Horrie was put in the hole. Featherstone had first watch just to make sure he kept quiet. Part two of Plan A was successful, so far. But it was the beginning of an arduous project that went on for several days, and included spot inspections by officers. Had Horrie absorbed that even when an officer whose scent he did not recognise entered the tent, he was not to make a sound? It would be a tough test, for his instinct always was to protect the Rebels' territory.

21
JOURNEY TO THE DESERT'S EDGE

One late afternoon, Lieutenant Hewitt and another officer, Captain Ken Bartholemew, who had just joined the battalion from Australia, marched into the Rebels' tent unannounced. They were accompanied by Horrie's old enemy, Sergeant-of-the-Guard Ross Fitzgerald. The 49-year-old Duntroon-trained Bartholemew was said to be from military intelligence but no one knew why he was in the Middle East. He was short, rotund and with a similar appearance to King Edward VII, the (current) King George VI's grandfather, right down to the neat beard. All the Rebels were present, either playing cards or fiddling with radio equipment. They stood to attention. The captain had only recently heard about Horrie's exploits from Hewitt, who observed, rather than took part in, the inspection.

'So you're the infamous rabble known as the Rebels,' he said, 'the little group of signallers with the biggest AWL and brawling reputation of the Gunners.'

Each Rebel was nervous and most suspicious of Fitzgerald's presence. Had he come to find Horrie? Had he heard a rumour about the hidden dog and informed on them? Moody prayed that Fitzgerald's scent would not cause Horrie to growl or bark. The captain began by inspecting kits. He put his nose into Moody's bag.

'Ugh!' he said. 'You've had a dog in here, Private, have you not?'

'Yes, sir,' Moody said, his eyes so fixed on Fitzgerald that the big man looked away and began fossicking under beds. 'Donated him to the local police a week ago, sir.'

'Very noble of you,' the captain said.

'Be careful, Sergeant,' Fitzsimmons warned Fitzgerald. 'I handed in all Private Murchison's snakes for destruction, but one big asp slipped away. We think he may come "home," so to speak, every so often.'

Fitzgerald got off his knees, indicating he was not fond of reptiles. The thorough inspection went on for 18 minutes.

'I must say you lot have come a long way from the slovenly beginning in the Western Desert,' Hewitt said, pointing to the neat piles of packs and equipment lined up with centimetre perfection at the end of each bed. 'Must give credit to Sergeant Brooker, and you too, Corporal Featherstone.'

'I think you should know,' Captain Bartholemew said, hauling himself up straight and eyeballing Moody, 'that your precious little doggie went AWL from the police station a few nights ago.'

'I am sorry to hear that, Captain. We thought he had such a good home there.' Moody looked around at the other Rebels, who shrugged and sighed. 'Perhaps we should organise a search party to look—'

'That's enough, Private Moody,' the captain snapped, 'you will do nothing of the sort. If the dog is lost, it's a good thing for him, for I am a very good shot at a distance or close range.' He paused as if for theatrical effect and added: 'I am told by the Sergeant-of-the-Guard here that the dog—'

'Horrie, Captain,' Hewitt said, 'that is his name.'

'Yes, well, whatever you call him, he may well turn up at your tent, so we shall keep a look out.'

'I'm sure Private Moody will hand him in if he does,' Hewitt reassured the captain with a salute as the three men left the tent. Several of the Rebels fell back on their beds and groaned.

'That bloody Fitzgerald! What the hell was he doing at the inspection?!' the Shegog asked in disgust. 'He's not our sergeant.'

'Poppa is away on assignment for the day,' Harlor informed them.

'Someone should take Gerry out into the desert and shoot *him*,' Shegog muttered as he reached for his whisky flask. There was silence for a moment. The others began rolling cigarettes or filling pipes to calm their nerves. Darkness was falling.

'Horrie needs a reward,' Moody said after lighting up. He slid his bed and the concealing mattress aside. He lifted the boards and Horrie took two leaps and a scramble with his paws at the lip of the hole to hoist himself out. Moody waited until it was dark before wrapping him in a towel and walking to the edge of camp and a scrubby area where he let Horrie down to bound around for some much-needed exercise. Moody relit his pipe and made a mental note to record in his diary that he had just been through the tensest moment of the war for him. This included when bombs were dropping and Stukas were strafing in his direction. Not even the ride through Servia Pass in Greece held more terrors than the inspection. They were events where he could have been killed in any second. But that tent scrutiny of every nook and cranny had had his heart palpitating and his mind racing. He watched Horrie rooting around and then come bounding to him for a pat.

'You are worth it, mate,' he whispered as he bent down to pick him up, 'every second of hell we are putting you and ourselves through.'

Next trick was to train him to stay quiet in Moody's pack. This took up to two hours and must have been uncomfortable for Horrie. But he was dedicated to Moody and his directives, with complete trust in whatever these moves or games meant. He seemed aware that he just had to put up with them if he wanted to remain with the Rebels. After a few nights' work, Moody had only to place the pack on the ground and Horrie would attempt to climb into it himself. They practised on a route march, which was far more of a test in the heat of the day than the cool of the night. Despite his stoic efforts to remain still and quiet, Moody knew he had to be suffering, so he shaped a plywood frame to fit inside the pack. This allowed Horrie to sit up and stopped the pack from collapsing in on him. Moody then cut out the back portion of the pack, which rested against his (Moody's) back, and this allowed Horrie more air. The missing back portion was replaced by criss-crossed string to keep the dog from slipping out. Horrie seemed satisfied with the modified pack.

When the camp was disbanded early on 10 March 1942, Moody arranged for a friend and devout Horrie supporter, Barry the Butcher, to keep the dog hidden in the canteen until he could be picked up that night. Snug in the pack the following morning, Horrie left with the battalion, which moved to its Gaza embarkation point on the Palestine railroad. A piece of luck occurred when Moody and Gill were able to hitch a ride in the guard van on the train. Horrie jumped out of the pack and stretched his legs for the slow journey to Tewfik near the Egyptian border. He was placed back in the pack when the battalion alighted from the train and lined up for an evening meal. Moody was obligated to leave his pack with all the others. He went to some trouble arranging it so that Horrie was upright. Moody became aware of someone behind him, watching. It was Captain Bartholemew.

'Something precious in there, Private?' Bartholemew asked.

Moody thought his heart had missed a beat. He turned to face the captain without responding. The captain broke into a smile.

'I like dogs very much,' he said, dropping his voice, 'but keep him well out of sight. Not everyone feels like we do.'

Moody had never been more relieved. The captain had surprised him after his behaviour at the tent inspection, but he guessed it had been an act in front of Hewitt, who loved Horrie but would have to support his confiscation and killing, and Fitzgerald, who hated the dog and would love to have seen him executed.

At 7 a.m. on 12 March the Rebels prepared for the 6.5 kilometre march to the port of Tewfik. Moody was concerned that Horrie could wilt in the early morning heat. He had Gill carry him while Moody marched close behind, encouraging the dog all the way. This worked and the battalion rested in tents for the night, which allowed Moody to sneak him out for exercise again. Then came the final big test on the next day, which was particularly hot, when there was a final 6 kilometre march to the ship, the USS *West Point.* Gill carried him in his backpack again and Moody stepped close behind once more, whispering words of hoped-for comfort in the blazing heat, which had the dog panting. But he remained motionless. Every few hundred metres, Moody wet his fingers with his water bottle and poked them through the top of the pack. Horrie licked them, and Moody could hear his tail swishing against the plywood.

They reached the wharf and looked up at the mighty ship, which had been the USA's answer to the UK's *Queen Mary*. It would carry about 8000 Australian troops, mainly from 6th Division, including more than 600 from the 2/1 Machine Gun Battalion. Horrie was still panting when Gill placed him on the dock in the face of a light breeze that gave him some relief.

'Now for the biggest worry of all,' Moody muttered to Gill, 'the final inspection.'

But there wasn't one. Moody picked up the pack for the small boat ferry to the USS *West Point* manned by American sailors. By some judicious manipulation and promises of alcohol, which was forbidden on this ship, Moody and Gill commandeered a cabin with a shower. The six beds in it would be taken by Rebels. There was still much covering up to do and no risk could be taken, but Horrie could run free in the crowded cabin among close friends.

'You are a very lucky little fella,' Fitzsimmons said, tapping his nose, 'you are on the way to Australia!'

22
THE FAST TRIP HOME

There was some concern that a German U-boat or Japanese submarine might attack and sink the USS *West Point.* It was meant to sail without escort south through waters that the Axis powers wished to dominate. But after cruising out of the Gulf of Eden it changed course and headed south along the east coast of Africa. Then it swung east towards Fremantle. Lights were forbidden at night to avoid the big converted carrier being spotted by the enemy. But concerns were fewer on the sail across the Indian Ocean, although the eccentric American Captain F. A. Kelly caused a little apprehension among the troops by deciding to run his gun crews through some exercises. These included throwing targets overboard and circling them while firing for hours at a time as well as following a course away from Australia.

'He is showing us gunners how it's done,' Brooker observed, 'an impressive waste of ammunition.'

'And wasting precious hours in taking us home,' Harlor remarked.

Jut-jawed and aggressive Kelly did not endear himself to the diggers by decreeing that alcohol was forbidden on board. He claimed to Australian officers that he wanted everyone to be battle alert, and that booze would not allow this. But his dictatorial approach was no deterrent for the diggers, who had smuggled on board a range of alcoholic drinks, from quality champagne and Scotch to cheap beer. Even some Americans disobeyed the directive. Kelly, who strutted his ship like a maritime Caesar, also did not want any bad behaviour or brawling on board between the diggers and the American crew. He knew of fights on the Australian mainland between the two nationalities. But on the ship and in this situation of support, the Australians appreciated the Americans, including the number of African-Americans, for their friendly nature and music, especially jazz. In turn the Americans fitted into the spirit of things and played two-up with the diggers.

Rumours reached the Rebels that Kelly wanted a 'clean' ship with no pets on board. Captain Bartholemew took Moody aside on the deck one morning and confirmed the rumour.

'Kelly's a fastidious type,' the captain said, 'a bit inflexible and a strict disciplinarian. It's not like being on a

Pommie ship, which is always a little slack. Kelly does not want to be second to anyone in terms of following laws, no matter how draconian, not just to the letter, but to the final syllable. He has heard that the other troop ships are about to take action against pets, so now he is too. If you hear of anyone with an animal, tell them to make sure it's not spotted.'

'Thank you, I will, Captain,' Moody said. 'If I may ask: the boys were wondering what your role is?'

'Let's just say the Curtin government wants a smooth liaison between the division and the Americans on the trip.'

'So you're a liaison officer?'

'Something like that,' Bartholemew replied, and then asked, 'Have you heard of anyone with a cat on board?'

'No, can't say I have,' Moody said with a reflective frown.

'Kelly hates cats. Says he will personally grab it by the tail, swing it over his head and launch it overboard, if one is found.'

'Hmm,' Moody mouthed reflectively, 'how does he feel about dogs?'

'Let's just say, not like us.'

This discussion kept the Rebels on alert. Horrie had to remain locked in the cabin with a minder, even during the heat when crossing the Equator. The Rebels fanned him and kept him cool with wet towels through the ordeal, but he seemed to take it all well, especially with the perpetual attention. The trip was easy compared to the trials he had been through in the pack, the hole in the ground and in

Stuka attacks. He was allotted the best spot in the cabin at night, underneath the inlet that supplied fresh air. Horrie had no trouble with the daily morning cabin inspection. He was even keen for the game of concealment in the pack, especially now that it was for no longer than five minutes.

With Horrie appearing safe, at least for the moment, Moody began to worry about Imshi, who was travelling back with the Anti-Tank Regiment on another ship. He spoke to Harlor in the Rebels' cabin.

'Could you get a message to another ship?' Moody asked him, knowing that if anyone could it would be Harlor.

'We're not allowed that luxury, I'm afraid. They say the Japs might pick up stray messages and pinpoint our location. I doubt it myself because we can create our own rogue codes, ship to ship, and the Japs wouldn't be able to work out what was what. But those are the rules.'

'Could you cosy up to some of the Yank signallers and push messages to and from McKellary? I'm concerned that he may not know Imshi is in danger.'

'I am already acquainted with the top signallers on board. They want me in the Signals room to talk engineering and radios all the time. Even I get bored!'

'See what you can do, mate, please.'

A few hours later, Harlor reported back to Moody: 'I got through, and received an odd response. Mac sent a strange message saying that Imshi had "disappeared."'

'Sounds ominous.'

'I sent a message back asking him to clarify, but there has been no further response. It could either mean that

Imshi has been destroyed, or that Mac is covering his arse with the message, indicating that Imshi has been well hidden.'

*

On 23 March, Brooker was walking up the steps to the top deck when he noticed Sergeant Fitzgerald and Captain Bartholemew in earnest discussion deep along a corridor. Brooker informed Moody, who went to see Bartholemew in his cabin near the sergeant's quarters.

'Yes, Fitzgerald came to me,' Bartholemew admitted, 'but I can't disclose the substance of the conversation.'

'But does he know about Horrie?' Moody asked.

'No, he only suspects Horrie is on board. He has no proof, and nor do I.'

'So he was urging you to—'

'As I said, Private, it was a privileged conversation. But I will say that Captain Kelly is set to assert his authority over pets on board. My advice is to stick to your story, and don't change it.'

After 12 days at sea, Kelly summoned Lieutenant Jim Hewitt, Brooker and Moody to his office in the captain's cabin. Already there and looking distraught was Sergeant Bill McMillan, the owner of Ooboo the cat, and the Americans in charge of onboard discipline: the ship's adjutant, Major Harrison, and the ship's master-at-arms, C. P. O. Radcliffe. Kelly began with a lecture about cleanliness, animal diseases, particularly rabies, and Australia's strict quarantine laws for flora and fauna. He ended with a tirade about him having strict orders to destroy all animals on 'my ship before disembarking anywhere in Australia.'

Just as he finished a sustained burst of warnings about 'the dire consequences for disobeying me,' Captain Bartholemew slipped into the office.

'Having said all that,' Kelly continued, his face flushed and pointing at McMillan, 'I am giving you two hours to round up your cat and hand him in. If you don't do this, I shall not berth in Australia. How will your fellow Australians feel about that? Deliver one stupid cat or they don't go home!'

McMillan began to say something and stopped himself. Instead he saluted and backed out of the cabin.

'All this trouble over one goddamned cat!' Kelly fumed. He turned his attention to the new arrivals. 'Now I know there is a dog on board. I want it produced, otherwise, gentlemen, this ship will not dock. I mean it!'

'Captain Kelly,' Bartholemew said, 'none of those gentlemen seem to know if there is a dog—'

'I have been told about it!' Kelly snapped. 'Horrie . . . the er . . . Wog . . . or something. What's a "wog" anyway?'

'It's a term the Australians used for Arabs in general. Can be a term of endearment, at times.'

'I don't care what it is. Produce the animal!'

'Sir,' Bartholemew began again, 'there is a distinct difference between the alleged cat and the alleged dog.'

'I know,' Kelly said, breaking into a twisted grin, 'one can climb trees and the other barks, right?'

Bartholomew laughed politely.

'Not exactly, Captain. The cat, I am told, was just an adored part of one company; a pet. Whereas I am led to believe that the alleged dog was an important part of an entire machine gun battalion.' He began describing the reports of Horrie's activities in saving lives but Kelly cut him short. He was furious.

'When you do produce this goddamned dog,' he said, 'I am not going to throw it overboard. I am going to throw it in the ship's furnace!'

The cabin fell silent. From his manner, no one disbelieved him.

'May I say something, Captain,' Moody said, stepping forward and introducing himself, 'I know there was much feeling towards this alleged—'

'So you admit there is a dog, Private?'

'No, sir, I am just reporting to you something very important about the mood of the boys of my battalion. They are close-knit and very tough men, sir. Very experienced fighters. If this dog exists and has done all the things claimed, including saving the lives of every one of them, then they will not take kindly to any threat to er . . . do what you just said, sir.'

Kelly took a step towards Moody. 'Is that some kind of threat, son?' he asked, his manner fearsome.

'No,' Hewitt interjected, 'Private Moody is trying to help you run a peaceful ship, Captain. There may be trouble if any alleged dog is harmed. And none of us want disharmony on your excellent vessel.'

Kelly's face boiled. Even his ears went red. But before

he could explode, Bartholemew intervened: 'And harmony is my job, as you know, Captain . . .'

Kelly ignored Bartholemew and stepped closer to Moody. The captain looked as if he might strike him.

'I want to hear from you, Private,' he said, pointing at Moody with force, 'what you are saying will happen if I throw the dog in the furnace!'

'If there is a dog, Captain,' Moody said, staring back at Kelly, 'and if you throw it in the furnace . . .'

'Come on, son, out with it!'

'With respect, Captain, the men of my battalion are wild enough, when pushed to the limits, to dish out similar treatment. I am only letting you know, not as a threat, but as one who has been with these hard men fighting against the Nazis in Greece and Crete. I am only trying to be helpful. No one wants trouble. Not this close to home.'

Kelly gaped. His face drained.

'Did you say "similar treatment"? Are you suggesting that they would throw me in the furnace?!' the captain asked in a mixed tone of haughtiness and anger.

'I don't think Private Moody meant that,' Bartholomew said in a placatory tone.

'No, no,' Hewitt said, 'he didn't mean that, Captain.'

'But I did mean that,' Moody said, 'not as a threat, but as an *explanation* of the consequence of any such action.' Hewitt dismissed Moody and led him and Brooker out of the office, leaving Bartholemew to deal with the seething captain.

*

Kelly could not be calmed down. He slowed the ship until it was dead in the water and in sight of the mainland. The passengers soon learnt why they were not continuing into Fremantle. The ship sat in the water for four hours. After further threats and intimidations, Bill McMillan felt the pressure of the 8000 diggers enticingly in sight of Australia and their families and friends. He finally submitted Ooboo, in a cage, to the adjutant, Major Harrison.

'I think you'd better not see this,' the adjutant said. McMillan was visibly distressed. He hurried below deck. Harrison summoned the master-at-arms, Radcliffe, and handed the cage containing the unsuspecting Ooboo to him. Radcliffe then took the caged pet to the top deck and threw the cage over the side of the ship. He watched it sink below the waves, before reporting his duty done to the adjutant, who then told Kelly.

'Good,' Kelly remarked, 'then to engines, Mr Adjutant, and full steam ahead for Fremantle.' A day later, Bartholomew got word to Moody to visit his cabin in secret, and he told him: 'I just wanted to let you know that Captain Kelly is not going to make any special search for that, er . . . alleged dog. Amidst all the bluff and bluster, he took your word of caution seriously, although he would never admit it. His little face-saving comment was that he wanted the ship to remain a harmonious one so close to our boys making it home.'

'You don't know how pleased I am to hear that, Captain, thank you.'

'Of course, he could boast that he got his way with poor Ooboo.'

'It's a pity we could not have saved the cat. He was a special, brave little fella. Didn't see much of him because he and Horrie weren't close. But on all accounts from C Company, he was terrific.'

'What an ego that Kelly has! Stops his ship off the coast to put pressure on 8000 diggers, who've given their all for their country and the Allied cause in combat! All over a sweet little moggie!'

'I just wondered how you managed to persuade him not to keep his threat to find and burn Horrie?'

'I really just extended or modified your words. I emphasised again Horrie's importance to the battalion. I reminded him of how fit he thought the gunners were when he saw them exercising on the deck; how some, although not all, had their weapons with them. I sowed the seed of what even the mildest munity on his ship would do to his reputation and how it would look from far-off US Military HQ in Washington; how the publicity would paint him as, using the American colloquialism, "the bad guy" for throwing innocent little pets overboard. He knew it was my job to deal with this sort of thing and keep the peace. After the steam stopped coming out of his ears, he saw my point of view.' Bartholemew paused and chuckled. 'But it was your wonderful, gutsy bluff that really put the wind up his kilt.' He scrutinised Moody's face. 'It was a bluff, wasn't it?'

'No,' Moody said, 'it wasn't. I canvassed many members of the battalion, not just my platoon. They have no particular allegiance to Captain Kelly. But they do to Horrie. If he was killed the way described, I don't just *believe* they would take similar action against the captain; I *know* it.'

Bartholemew blinked. He was stunned. After a few seconds he raised his eyebrows and nodded. 'Just a word in advance so if anything happens it does not come as a shock to you,' he said, 'Captain Kelly will be making out a report on the events that occurred in his cabin. Your remarks will figure in that report. There may be repercussions if your words about throwing him in the furnace are taken seriously by the Australian authorities.'

'I wouldn't be surprised.'

'Yes, but these things always look worse on paper. Some petty little Canberra bureaucrat might wish to demonstrate his power.'

'I really don't care. I just want to put two feet on Aussie soil.'

'You mean *six* feet,' Bartholemew said, with a grin.

*

The USS *West Point* stopped at Fremantle on 26 March 1942 to let the Western Australian diggers and gunners off and there was no shore leave for the rest. The Americans were making their presence felt. Catalina flying boats could be seen wobbling into their new base at Crawley Bay on Perth's Swan River. American soldiers were putting up anti-aircraft guns on Fremantle Wharf. The USS *Pengrove* could be seen sailing away from the dock to make way for the huge USS *West Point* after depositing an advance contingent of the US 197th Coastal Artillery, which had both machine gunners and artillery men. All this activity drove it home to the new arrivals of the 6th Division that they were most likely to be back in action soon.

It was an important time for American–Australian relations. Across the other side of the country on the same day, General Blamey, Australia's top military commander, arrived from the Middle East to meet American General Douglas MacArthur, who would be the Allied commander in the Pacific leading the counterattack to the Japanese dominance in the region.

The next morning *West Point* anchored at Port Adelaide and there was to be no kit inspection before leaving the ship. It seemed that Captain Kelly was not concerned any more with what the diggers carried once they left his charge.

The Rebels, as they had done in several countries, closed ranks around Moody and his pack as they walked down the gangway, just in case there was a last-minute hitch. But there was none. The battalion was marched to the picturesque Adelaide Cricket Oval where they would have temporary billets. Once there, Moody released a grateful Horrie. Much to the delight of clapping and cheering Rebels and gunners, his first act on Australian soil was to race straight for the nearest gum tree.

23

THE CONTINUING COVER-UP

The Rebels voted that Horrie should become the sole responsibility of Moody, although they all made a pledge to do what they could to protect the dog, should there be trouble over their schemes to secrete him into Australia. As soon as Moody was granted leave in mid-April 1942 he took Horrie by train to Melbourne to stay with his father Henry in East St Kilda. Henry had taught his son much about dogs and he had an immediate rapport with Horrie, despite his civvies. A companion of Henry's, Dianne Winslow, wasn't so fortunate. Horrie still had a blind spot about females, or as Moody pointed out, 'anyone in a dress.'

'Remember, he only ever knew "family" from men in Australian uniform and slouch hats,' Moody tried to explain to Dianne, who disliked being cornered by a growling, snarling Horrie. 'His vision of the enemy was anyone in Arab garb—you know, long flowing robes—and by extension, people in dresses.'

'I'm not switching to long pants for him or you or anyone,' Dianne said with some indignation.

'He's a real war dog; a true warrior,' Moody told Henry and Dianne. 'He has been bombed, strafed, and probably beaten in his first few months. He is on a state of war footing just like me, except that I can't take him with me any more. We'll be fighting up in the islands pretty soon, or at least that's the drum.'

'Well I wish you'd take him with you,' Dianne said. 'Those eyes when he is angry! They are aflame, like the devil's!'

It took much cajoling by father and son for Dianne to come around to accepting Horrie's hostility. The dog was not coming halfway and refused to go near her. It was fortunate that Dianne did not live with Henry and only he could feed or take him for a walk down to nearby Green Meadow Gardens. Dianne made sure she was never alone when she visited the Moody home. She was not the only one experiencing Horrie's wrath. The local milkman, in his white uniform, and his horse and cart received a working over. The postman on his bike had to run the gauntlet every day in the otherwise aptly named Meadow Street. Horrie would streak out of number 28 and make a dive for the postman's ankle. The postman complained and, when Horrie was kept in the house one day, he asked Moody about the dog's breed.

'He's a er . . . terrier-cross,' Moody replied, being careful not to add the word 'Egyptian.'

'I'd call him a very cross terrier,' the postman remarked, his eyes flicking to the Moodys' front yard, as if he expected the low-flying white missile to appear any moment.

'He's only been around since you've been home,' the postman added suspiciously. 'You didn't pick him up in Africa or the Middle East, did you?'

'No. It's a family pet left with us now.'

'Pet? Mate, I've been nipped by plenty of dogs, but yours has the sharpest teeth. He left me with lacerations last time. If it happens again, I'll have to tell the police and they'll put him down.'

Henry and Moody responded by making sure that Horrie was kept inside or chained up when the postman made his daily run.

The serious threat from Japanese invasion, first on Australian-controlled territory in New Guinea and Papua, and also on the mainland, continued through April and Moody received orders to make his way to Ingleburn south of Sydney for a reassembling of the battalion. His parting from Horrie was a difficult moment. Man and dog had been more or less inseparable during nearly all of the dog's 15 months of life. Moody was consoled by knowing that Horrie had a good home and would be looked after royally. But the little dog remained agitated when he noticed Moody preparing his kit. He tried to climb into the pack, and was annoyed not to be allowed to do so. Horrie refused to eat his food and had a mournful expression on his sensitive face the evening before Moody was due to leave. The next morning, when an army truck arrived, Henry had Horrie on a leash. The dog barked and howled in protest as Moody boarded the truck and waved goodbye.

*

On 4 May 1942, the Rebels were together again, except for Murchison, whose fate or whereabouts were still unknown, although the group had heard rumours that he had been in action in Java against the Japanese as a member of the 7th Division. But still, half a year after he swapped divisions to see action, there was no definitive word on his fate or whereabouts. Rumours in war were so frequent that they were often discounted.

Just after some heavy rain on the Ingleburn camp, Moody, Gill and Bruce McKellary went for a long walk on a bush road. It was a cool May evening. Bush smells of eucalypts, acacias and other flora mingled. A kangaroo bounded from the bush 30 metres ahead. A kookaburra made its distinctive cry and another answered.

'Isn't it great to be laughed at by birds again?' Moody remarked.

'Not for long,' McKellary responded. 'You blokes will be pushed up to Moresby. But I don't know what will happen with us. The Japanese prefer bikes to tanks. Our regiment may even be disbanded.'

'Don't think so,' Gill said. 'They won't use tanks in New Guinea. But if the Japs hit the mainland you will be needed all right.'

'You got Horrie in okay, we hear,' McKellary said with a sly grin. 'Heard a rumour that you threatened to throw the ship's captain in the furnace after he threatened to do that to Horrie.'

'Not quite the way it happened,' Moody mumbled.

'That's the long and short of it,' Gill said.

'Jesus! I didn't have the guts to do that!' McKellary said.

'Did you get Imshi in?' Moody asked.

McKellary looked around as if someone might hear him. But there was nobody in sight. 'Quarantine officials are bastards,' he said. 'We got her off the ship, then took a train to Melbourne and had to make a cops-and-robbers dash with her to a safe house in Collingwood. We just squeezed her out a back-gate when two blokes in suits arrived with two cops to "arrest" her.'

'Is she safe now?'

'Oh, yeah. Smuggled her to a mate in the country.'

Moody smiled and clapped McKellary on the back.

'That's terrific!'

'But I can't be with her. Not while I'm in service.'

'Same for me. Horrie's with my father in Melbourne. I miss the little blighter already.'

'Cops would love to have arrested me, but they had no evidence I'd ever had her. I stuck to the story that she had disappeared on the ship. Told them I suspected someone had thrown her overboard. They asked a lot of questions about how I picked her up; where she had been with the regiment. They took a lot of notes. I kept it vague.'

'Vague is good,' Gill observed.

'Yes, and sticking to a good story and a good plan,' Moody added.

'You know, Moods,' McKellary said, with a smile of admiration, 'you'd make a good general, especially telling a bastard Yank ship commander you'd throw him in a furnace! You're a legend!'

'Pity I'm just a lowly private.'

'Who loves dogs.'

*

A second front loomed closer for the 6th Division as a mighty sea fight—the Battle of the Coral Sea—took place on 7-8 May 1942 just off Australia's north-east coast. The Japanese had been on their way to take New Guinea's important south coast port at Moresby, but an American-Australian armada intercepted them. While losses were about even, the Allies won an important strategic victory by preventing the enemy from reaching Moresby. It was more than a blood-nose for the Japanese admiralty and the first setback in its six months rule of the Pacific Ocean. Yet it didn't stop Japan's relentless military drive and on 31 May, three midget submarines attacked Sydney Harbour with the aim of sinking the battle cruiser USS *Chicago.* Launched from a mother submarine, the midgets penetrated the harbour's slack defences. They missed their target but caused much chaos, including the torpedoing of an Australian service ship, *Kuttabul,* killing 21 on board.

The 2/1 Machine Gun Battalion at Ingleburn was fully operational but was only alerted the next morning after the wild night on Sydney Harbour in which the midget subs attacked and onshore and ship defences retaliated.

When Brooker, Fitzsimmons, Moody and Gill were in Ingleburn buying newspapers in the morning, a breathless newsagent told them the rumours about the subs in the Harbour hours earlier.

'Yeah, well,' Fitzsimmons said, looking at the headlines that had nothing about the attack, 'can't have been too bad; hasn't made the front page.'

'But it's really serious, isn't it?' the newsagent asked.

He and a few other customers in the shop looked surprised, even shocked, by the careless attitude of these men in uniform. Seeing this, Brooker remarked for all to hear: 'It's not like waves of Luftwaffe attacking with bombs and machine guns. I mean every day. That's what we call *serious.*'

24

TO THE FRONT AND BACK

In June 1942, a month after the Battle of the Coral Sea, the Americans and the Japanese fought a mighty sea battle at Midway in the Pacific, which looked to be a defining conflict in the Pacific War. The USA inflicted a major defeat on the Japanese navy, which had to retreat, lick its wounds and rebuild. This pushed the pendulum of power in the Japanese military hierarchy back to the Japanese army. It wrested back its prime position in its battles with the Allies, and the Japanese navy was forced to play a less significant role for the first time in the Pacific War.

Prime Minister Tojo, who doubled as Army Minister, continued with his plans to invade and take over the Australian territory of Papua and also its League of Nations–mandated territory of New Guinea. He ordered his army forces to invade Papua's north coast on 21 July 1942, in the month *following* the pivotal Battle of Midway. This led to both the 6th and 7th Divisions fighting in four major encounters supported by militia (conscripted) battalions.

The Rebels were part of the battalion's contingent shipped to Deception Bay on the coast north of Brisbane in August 1942. Moody and Gill grew restless and decided to go AWL in an attempt to join forces who were about to fight against the Japanese in Papua. They stole off in the night on motorbikes and took several days to reach Brisbane. They were there several months in which they wrote and read a lot, and practised their skills at two-up, so well 'taught' by Fitzsimmons, and their card skills, which had been honed in tight games with the 'shark' Murchison. Gill and Moody became caught up in a string of two-up and card games on a wild New Year's Eve with 7th Division soldiers on their last night in Australia before being shipped to New Guinea. Both men had 'lucky' streaks that had been helped along by the tricks they'd learnt. They accepted 'payment' in the form of them being smuggled on board the SS *Tasman*, which sailed for Port Moresby on New Year's Day 1943, and then on to Papua's eastern tip at Milne Bay soon afterwards. The Battle of Milne Bay had been over for several months but there was still some 'mopping up' to do of rogue Japanese groups. Moody had a bad start when he was shot in the knee on his first day in the area. But after having the wound treated he was incapacitated for only a week before again catching up with Gill in the search west for the still-fighting Japanese groups.

After four months involved with forward units of 7th Division, the two went AWL yet again and returned to Brisbane for their own kind of maverick leave from the front. Bored with this after less than six weeks, they bluffed their way into another 7th Division unit of soldiers about to be shipped on the *Duntroon* to Port Moresby, but not before trying, in June 1943, to transfer officially to the 7th Division. Otherwise, they would not be paid for their efforts. Moody and Gill were advised by Major Dunkley, the 7th's administrative commander, that their application had to be submitted through their 'parent unit,' which meant the 2/1 Machine Gunners. To their surprise their transfer was accepted. The two Rebels once more joined the fighting, this time on Papua's northern shores.

When not in the action, Moody spent time rewriting his lost dairies that had gone down with the *Costa Rica* off Crete. He had approached book publisher Angus & Robertson and they had commissioned author Ion Idriess to write a story based on Moody's diaries. Idriess had written about Anzacs in the Middle East in World War I. Moody would send batches of the new version of his diaries to Henry, who would post them on to Sydney-based Idriess for embellishing into a narrative.

*

Over 19 months from 1942 to 1944 the Japanese poured more than 200,000 troops into New Guinea and Papua, attacks that were met by the diggers at Kokoda in Papua's north, then Milne Bay on Papua's east coast, followed by Buna, Sananada and Gona in Papua's north. The final enemy thrust was at Lae and Finschhafen on New Guinea's north coast. It was an Australian defence of its 'doorstep' territories, with American troops playing a support role. When the Japanese were eventually pushed back by early 1944, Moody and Gill managed for the last time to leave Moresby in February for Brisbane. Then in April, Moody obtained leave, with several warrants and charges pending, to see his parents and Horrie in Melbourne.

A few days before Moody was due to return, Henry gave the little dog a sock belonging to Moody, which had not been washed since he left home two years earlier.

'Jim will be home soon,' he said, playing with the sock, 'Jim will be home soon.'

Horrie's stump would straighten and he would wag it for a moment, and look at Henry as if to say: *I'll believe it when I see him.* On the morning of his expected return, Henry took the dog and friend Dianne to Spencer Street Station by train to wait for his son, who was coming by rail overnight from Sydney. About 20 diggers in uniform were there to greet fellow servicemen. Horrie, on a leash, wanted to stop and wag his tail at every man. Most diggers reached down to pat him and some noticed his colour patch and tag with the marking EX.I 2/1 M/G Bn.

'Is he Horrie?' one young digger asked in surprise. Henry nodded.

'I've heard about him!'

The digger mentioned his identity to others and several crowded around, making a fuss of him. Horrie had a spring in his step.

'I've never seen him so happy,' Dianne said with a bemused look.

Henry and Dianne sat on platform seats. The crowd of greeting relatives and friends grew. Horrie became excited five minutes before the train was due in.

'I think he knows why we are here,' Henry observed. 'He was on plenty of trains in North Africa and Palestine.'

'I am beginning to understand a little more now,' Dianne remarked. 'He really shows love towards those boys.'

'They're all he knew until he was a year old. They're his family.'

'He's still looking at them, wagging his tail.'

'C'mon, Dianne, you get on with him now.'

'Oh, yes, but he is never animated like that when I visit you. Although he is nice enough these days. It has taken me a lot of cajoling, and being extra-nice to him, without any return for a long time!'

'You've come a long way since he snarled at you on sight, and he's okay with anyone else in civvies now.'

'He just ignores them,' Dianne said with a laugh, 'even your postman can say hello without Horrie getting off the front porch.'

'That's because we feed him too much. He's too fat!'

The incoming train's whistle blew. Horrie sat facing it, his ears erect.

'Perhaps he thinks it's a Stuka,' Henry whispered to Dianne.

When Moody, kit on his back, stepped off the train, his father did not recognise him for a split-second because of his limp. Then Henry let the dog off the leash. Horrie scurried, a little slower now, aged three years, to Moody. But the dog was even more enthusiastic in his greeting than ever. Horrie's bigger derrière swung in circles around his master. Moody's eyes welled up as he bent to cuddle Horrie and then hoist him up into his arms. The dog smothered him with licks. He yelped his appreciation.

'You remember me,' Moody said, wiping away tears, 'you fat little bugger! You remember!'

Two soldiers took photos of the reunion.

Moody kissed Dianne, with Horrie still squirming with delight in his arms. Moody put him on the ground and shook hands with his father.

'How'd you get that limp?' Henry asked.

'It's nothing.'

'Were you wounded?'

'I'll tell you about it later.'

'If it's a war wound,' Henry remarked, 'you can get a medical discharge. I'm told it's a little easier now the Japs have been pushed back.'

'Don't listen to all the propaganda from Macarthur. He's just obsessed with his grand plan to "return" to the Philippines. The Nips are still in New Guinea and the other islands in big numbers. We'll have more to do than those stupid press reports here are saying about "mopping up." The journalists should fly up there and have a look. But of course they're not allowed.'

'So you are going back up?' Dianne asked.

'Maybe.'

'Till when? The war could go on for years.'

'Till the job is done or I get bored.'

Horrie interrupted the conversation by pawing at Moody.

'Sorry, Horrie, old warrior!' Moody said, picking him up again. 'Didn't mean to leave you out of the conversation!'

*

Moody reacquainted himself with Horrie and joined his father one morning walking the dog down to the nearby Balaclava Road shopping centre in East St Kilda to pick up the magazine *Smiths Weekly*. Horrie carried it home in his mouth.

'You know the old saying,' Henry said, '"you can't teach an old dog new tricks"? Well Horrie is the exception. Of all the wonderful dogs we've had, and we've had some brilliant ones over the decades, he is the smartest.'

On returning home, they met the postman at their front gate. Horrie growled at him for the first time in a year.

'What's that about?' the postman asked, keeping an eye on the dog.

'He's a bit excited since seeing diggers on the Spencer Street platform a week ago, and me being home,' Moody explained. 'Just being his protective self. Thinks he's in a combat zone again. Nothing personal.'

'So he did come from overseas?'

Moody hesitated before saying: 'It's a long story, Bill. You'll be able to read about it soon.'

'Speaking of diggers,' the postman said, handing Moody a letter, 'there's something official-looking here for you.'

Inside the house, Moody opened the letter. It was from the Department of the Army. He had been charged with 'Firing on the King's enemy, without the King's consent.' The letter explained the odd charge was for him not being officially part of any unit when involved in Papua battles on his first 'tour' there. Moody had to explain it to Henry, who was not too pleased about his son's rebellious behaviour in going AWL so often and the number of warrants for his arrest in his never-ending defiance of authority. Moody showed him the letter and pointed out the last line, which said: 'This charge is deferred until hostilities against the King's enemies cease.'

Henry was not placated.

'Won't look good on your war record,' he warned his son, 'along with all your other AWL charges. And let's not forget what you've done with Horrie and beating quarantine.'

'I'll worry about that when "hostilities cease,"' Moody said.

'You have to look ahead, son,' Henry went on. 'How are you going to gain employment if your war record is bad? And what about the soldier settlement scheme? The way you are going the government won't offer you any block; and if they do offer you something, it will be in woop-woop somewhere on land with rocks and unfertile soil. The government is far more authoritarian in wartime, son. It can be vindictive.'

'As I said, Dad,' Moody repeated, 'I'll worry about that when it's all over.'

*

The Japanese were in retreat by early 1945 but still willing to fight to the death of their last soldier, if the emperor so decreed. General Macarthur had implemented his plan of island hopping to skip north from Australia over Japanese garrisons in Java, Borneo, Bougainville, Singapore and other locations. He was commanding a combined US forces counterattack on the Japanese in the Philippines from where he was forced to flee to Australia in 1941, leaving his US–Filipino army of 22,000 leaderless and at the mercy of the enemy invaders. Now, more than three years later, Macarthur was determined to fight without the help of the experienced Australian 6th and 7th Divisions. He wanted the retaking of the Philippines and the defeat of the Japanese forces to be an exclusively US operation with him as the supreme commander. Macarthur had an inferiority complex to General Blamey, who until this point had a vastly superior record as a commander in both world wars. Macarthur feared Blamey's interference and desire to have diggers in the action, which would have caused the Americans to have to share some of the glory of victory.

Some diggers were relieved at their omission from the Pacific War's final stages. Others wished to fight on, either because they were so embedded as warriors and did not look forward to many prospects postwar, or because they wanted to see the war through to Japan's complete capitulation.

By mid-January 1945, part of the 2/1 Machine Gun Battalion was being wound down and the Rebels' Signals Unit was becoming increasingly redundant. All of the group decided to apply for discharge when they had the opportunity, and return to Sydney. Gill was interstate on a long, working holiday. For the moment, Moody took up residence at Silver Street in the south-west suburb of St Peters, which was the home of Gill's parents, who were also away interstate for several months. The recently discharged Brooker was temporarily lodging there too. Moody had plans to open a photography shop, first using the Silver Street, St Peters address for a business: 'Gilroy-Moody, specialists in Home Study Portraiture.' (Later he moved to Birkley Road, Manly, with Leica Snaps.) Moody also wished to be involved in the publication that the Sydney-based Ion Idriess had been working on.

Moody took the train to Melbourne and returned to Sydney with Horrie, being careful to gain a health certificate from the stock inspector before boarding the train in Melbourne. The second reunion, after another year apart, was heartfelt for both. Horrie, now more than four years of age, was still overweight but in good condition otherwise.

Moody met the lean, 55-year-old Idriess at a Sydney pub late in January 1945. It was mid-afternoon; quiet after the lunch-time crowd, and too early for the after-work rush to drink before 6 p.m. closing. There was just one drinker at the bar and he sat well away in a corner. Moody and Idriess had an immediate rapport. The author was prolific, having gathered his stories from his vast experience as a soldier, prospector and bushman. The book on Horrie was his twentieth in 18 years. Idriess' interests in photography, dogs, geology and history gave them much common ground. Most importantly, they had both served in the Middle East, with Idriess seeing action in World War I in the 5th Light Horse Regiment in Palestine and Syria. They could even compare war wounds. Idriess had been hit by shrapnel on Gallipoli while acting as a 'spotter' (someone who pointed out enemy targets) for the most accomplished sniper on Gallipoli, Billy Sing. Idriess had also taken a bullet at the Australian Light Horse's celebrated charge on Beersheba. After a wide-ranging discussion, Idriess suggested it would be 'terrific' if they could use Horrie in publicity for the book. Moody was circumspect.

'We need all the help we can get,' Idriess said. 'Have you seen the number of war titles coming out this year? Hundreds from the European war, and just as many from the Pacific campaign. And I can tell you, it won't stop. The Great War was the same. I tried to have my diaries published in 1920, but no one wanted to know. So many others, from General Monash down, were bringing out tomes. Didn't manage to see the dairies in print until '32—14 years after the war ended!'

'Not sure about exposing Horrie,' Moody said with a frown.

'The publisher is pushing me to persuade you—'

'Yes, well, you know the troubles I had when smuggling him in to Australia.'

'But if he was quarantined when he arrived . . . ?'

'He wasn't.'

'I've fudged it in the book.'

'I noticed.'

'It's a narrative style: not fiction, but not strictly non-fiction.'

They sipped their beers.

'The publisher wants to publish in May or June,' Idriess said, 'They want me photographed meeting Horrie.'

'That all sounds good. But I am worried about the quarantine people.'

'What could they do? Horrie's been here three years. They can only be concerned about him having rabies. The disease has a seven-month incubation period. He hasn't been frothing at the mouth and biting people, has he?'

'No,' Moody said with a smile, 'he gave up biting our postman a long time ago. Although the postie liked to talk a lot, he hasn't had more than thought bubbles coming out of his mouth.'

'I think the best thing is to go on the front foot. If we generate real public support for him—war dog warrior-hero and so on—the government won't take action. Once the story is out, there will be overwhelming support for him. They wouldn't dare do anything to the dear little fella. He's a national hero! I mean, what could they do? Push him into quarantine for a few weeks? Your old man says he is very healthy and never sick. That's what would be discovered and he'd be released.'

Moody scratched his head and sighed.

'You want the story out there, don't you?' Idriess prompted. Moody was still unsure. Idriess added: 'There is another angle. The Red Cross is having a fund-raiser. If we could put Horrie on show to raise money for that worthiest of causes, it would be great initial publicity. Then we can take it from there.' Moody's interest lifted. 'C'mon, Jim. You want to beat the competition, don't you?'

Moody remained non-committal, saying he would think about it.

That night, over more beers on the back porch of the Gill home, Moody told Brooker of Idriess' request.

'It's his business,' Brooker said, 'of course he wants Horrie to help with the publicity. But you must weigh up the risks. It will mean no skin off Idriess' nose if you get into trouble.' He paused to chuckle. 'Just more publicity!'

'I'm worried about all those damned government officials, especially quarantine.'

'Look, Idriess has a point. Once the Red Cross is behind it, and the press is positive, *and* the book is published, would they dare take you on? As he says, rabies is a non-issue. Horrie is clean. They're not going to confiscate a perfectly healthy animal three years after the event.'

'We need as much support as we can muster,' Moody frowned. 'Who else can we talk to?'

'Got it!' Brooker said, snapping his fingers. 'The RSL! We can organise Horrie to be made an honorary member! His war record would do it. They'd love a gimmick like that. And who would dare prosecute a war hero member of our illustrious Returned Services League?'

'But it doesn't even let Aborigines become members!'

'I know. I put up three of them after the Great War. They were excellent troopers in my regiment, but they were not accepted.'

'So why would they take in a canine member?'

'I reckon it's worth a try.'

'It would have to be the Melbourne RSL. Not here. I don't want all the focus on him in Sydney.'

'I'll see what I can do . . .'

'I'd feel a lot better if the RSL was with us.'

25

RED CROSS, BLACK MARK

The Melbourne RSL agreed to put Horrie's application as a fully fledged member to its membership at its monthly meeting on 3 February 1945. Before the vote, which was a jovial exercise, former and current serving men and women debated his suitability. Brooker's testimony about Horrie saving the life of every single soldier in his battalion, and many more men of the 6th Division on innumerable occasions, caused the debate to take on a more serious, if surreal atmosphere. A combination of humour, flowing beer and many compelling facts about Horrie's service saw an overwhelming vote in his favour.

It was the moment that Moody agreed to bring him into the open after Horrie's three years as a fugitive. Moody was ready to present him to the world, complete with his coat, colour patch, Gunners' disc and identity tags, and now RSL badge. Angus & Robertson, the book publisher, arranged for press coverage and he was photographed wearing his RSL badge, with Brooker and Moody in papers around the nation. One had the caption: 'Veteran: Honorary Member of the Melbourne RSL, who has been in five campaigns, poses with his owner, Jim Moody, discharged AIF, and Sergt. Roy Brooker.'

The accompanying articles were the beginning of what seemed to be a superb public relations exercise. Each piece mentioned his 'amazing,' 'incredible' war career. There was careful mention of his war wound (caused by the splinter on the *Lossiebank*) and that he was in fine health, which was a pointer to any quarantine official disposed towards pinning the possibility of rabies on him. A day later, Idriess turned up at the Gill home to meet Horrie and be photographed by the papers. The following morning, the coverage was again strong, with the grinning author snapped shaking Horrie's paw. Articles focused on Idriess' coming book.

The Gill home was flooded with calls from more journalists, many 6th battalion members, other soldiers and well-wishers. The sudden nationwide reaction worried Moody. At the dinner table that night, he discussed with Brooker the need for a back-up plan, should things go awry.

'We've had one everywhere for him,' Moody said, handing Horrie a scrap.

'But that was when we were at war,' Brooker said.

'We still are, mate.'

'What do you suggest?'

'A series of safe houses we can put him in. Ultimately he'd end up in Victoria, but not here if they come looking for him.' Moody thought for a moment. 'I have had one place in mind for three years.'

'Where?'

'Cudgewa.'

'Where?'

'Exactly. No one has heard of it. It's a one-rabbit town.'

'Where is it?'

'Near Corryong in north-east Victoria.'

'What's there?'

'I have a good mate from the battalion, Eddie Bennetts, who is a dairy farmer and rabbit-trapper there. Eddie reckons Horrie saved his life about four times. He offered to keep him safe if there was trouble.'

*

Moody was further fortified by the Kennel Club in Sydney, whose secretary wrote to him on 17 February telling how they would boost publicity further in conjunction with the Red Cross at the 1945 Easter Show to be held from 31 March to 2 April. They planned to put Horrie in a stall at the Lady Gowrie Red Cross Home. 'A post-card with his photograph and a short history' would be 'sold by a bevy of smart girls.'

*

On 24 February, a set of press articles on Horrie reached the desk of Mr Ron W. Wardle, the director of the Division of Veterinary Hygiene, in the Department of Health, Canberra. February 1945 had been a slow month in the somnolent capital, which had followed an even more sleepy January. The only news that alerted the isolated federal capital was the health of the Prime Minister John Curtin. His heart attack of late 1944 had worried the nation, but he had been driven by his chauffeur from hospital in Melbourne to the Lodge in Canberra and had pronounced himself fit for work. Few believed him but as Wardle helped look after the health of the animal population, there was little he could do for the nation's leader. But he could do something about the animal called Horrie, who had been ushered into Australia in 1942. Reading between the quaintly placed lines by journalists, the astute Wardle could sniff the cover-up of an illegality. He told colleagues that the perpetrators of this crime had the gall to make it all public.

'What's so annoying,' he added, 'it's nothing more than a money-making stunt via the publication of a book. Well, we'll put a stop to that.'

He alerted officers of the health department's quarantine station at Abbotsford, Sydney, and ordered them to find Moody and force him to give up the dog.

A few days later in the late afternoon, three officers turned up at 28 Silver Street in leafy St Peters and knocked on the door of the single-fronted home. Moody looked out a window. His instinct was that these men, two in white jackets, and one in a suit and tie, represented a major problem. He hurried to the back door to warn Brooker, who scooped up Horrie and whisked him out a back-gate and down a lane to a car. Horrie responded to directives to keep quiet. He loved the urgency, the running and being placed under a blanket in the back seat of a car. This was a sudden new 'game' and he loved the action. Brooker drove by the front of the Gills' home and saw Moody moving out onto the porch to talk to the three visitors. Brooker took the dog to another soldier's home in a pre-arranged plan.

Moody was told by the men from quarantine that they wished to detain Horrie for 'observations.' Moody claimed that the dog was in Melbourne.

'The photos in the paper were taken here in Sydney,' Mr John King of quarantine said while eyeballing Moody and looking for any 'deception' in his expression or answers.

'Yes, but we had to send him home by train.'

'Isn't he being put on display by the Red Cross in Sydney?'

'That's not for over a month.'

King kept staring. Moody held his gaze. After several seconds the interrogator asked: 'So you intend to retrieve him?'

'Not for a few weeks, but yes, that was my intention.'

King said the dog had to be delivered to quarantine as soon as possible and warned Moody of the 'very serious consequences' if he did not comply with the order.

King handed him a 'Seizure Form' for '1 dog—Egyptian Terrier.' The department representatives left and a half-hour later Brooker drove back to the Gills' home.

'I need a bloody beer!' Moody said, but not before ringing Idriess to tell him of the visit. Idriess was not stressed.

'That's all good,' he said. 'This will generate public support!'

'And draw attention to the book?'

'Of course! Don't worry. I can tell you from long experience in putting out books that this is a heaven-sent opportunity.'

'I'm not sure . . .'

'We can generate a real campaign in support of Horrie.'

'There is no way we can exhibit him now. I have to hand him in.'

'That's perfect! I'll let my contacts know. The publisher will back this change of tack for the book's promotion.'

Moody and Brooker went to a local pub. They consumed several beers recovering from the shock.

'I reckon they'll pressure me to produce Horrie fast,' Moody said. 'Why would they send three men to talk to me? They wanted to nab Horrie right there and then.'

'We must save him,' Brooker said.

'Always. I'll never let them have him, no matter what they threaten me with.'

'So we implement the Cudgewa plan?'

Moody nodded.

'Must be started tonight. We want him over the Victorian border as soon as possible.'

'You didn't even have a chance to say goodbye to him!'

'I was just becoming used to him being around, just like being back in the battalion.'

'You can catch up with him when all this settles down.'

'I hope so,' Moody said sadly as he took out his pipe and lit it. He puffed it to life and sighed. 'But after what happened today, I may never be able to have him with me again. The department will always have spies or checks. If he is ever found, they will take retribution for sure.' They were both contemplative for a few moments. 'Besides, he isn't a pup any more. He can't be run ragged as a fugitive at his age. He needs a stable home and environment.'

Brooker lit a cigarette. 'How will *you* avoid the quarantine demand?' he asked. 'They will send the cops after you for sure.'

'No problem about going AWL any more,' Moody said with a grin as he held up his glass of beer, 'at least that's over for me.'

'But you can't go on the run either.'

'I dunno. I could go bush and survive taking itinerant work.'

'You won't receive a war pension.'

'So what?'

'You can't cut off all those options by disappearing! What about your soldier settlement entitlement?'

'Doubt I'll get anything like that now.'

The two men drank and smoked in silence. They watched as the pub began to fill with patrons.

'There is something else I could do,' Moody said. 'I could find a Horrie look-alike and present him to quarantine.'

Brooker looked stunned.

'Where?'

'I'll comb all the pounds in Sydney.'

Brooker's expression brightened. 'Could you do that?' he asked in admiration. 'That would be brilliant!'

'If I do this,' Moody said, the cogs of his shrewd mind working overtime, 'we tell no one, only the Rebels.'

They clinked glasses.

'What about Idriess?' Brooker asked.

'No, can't risk telling him. I appreciate his keenness for the book to do well, and he certainly knows all there is to know about publicity. But he would probably want to put our "switch" of dogs in the story!'

'He would! That would make it a bestseller. A real twist in the tale!'

'Or t–a–i–l,' Moody said, indicating to the barman that they wanted two more beers.

'And your dad,' Brooker probed, 'will you tell him?'

'No. He won't go along with it. Only your tight-lipped Rebels should ever know our little scheme, Sergeant Brooker.'

'Agreed, Private Moody.'

*

The next morning, Friday 2 March, the pressure mounted. Quarantine's Mr King rang Moody to order him to produce Horrie in seven days.

'That should give you ample time to bring him up from Melbourne,' King said, 'if he is in Melbourne. If you don't comply with this directive, Mr Moody, you will be charged with several offences under section 68 of the Quarantine Act, 1908 to 1924. Do you want me to read them?'

'Yes, you can read them, but to yourself after we finish this phone call.'

There were a few seconds silence on the line.

'This is not a laughing matter, Mr Moody.'

'Do you think I'm laughing over an order to leave my dog with you? What are your plans for him, anyway?'

'He'll be put through a routine quarantine inspection.'

'And then, you will return him to me?'

'That is the normal procedure, if the dog is healthy. But that decision will be up to the director.'

'The director?'

'Mr Wardle.'

After the phone call, Moody found Brooker reading another article about Horrie in the *Sydney Morning Herald.*

'The bastards are going to put Horrie down,' Moody said.

'They said that?'

'No, but I can spot deception a mile off.'

'Because you are an expert?'

'Probably,' Moody said, picking up his car keys. 'C'mon. We are going on a search for Horrie's look-alike today. I'm taking my camera. We are going to document this.'

A few minutes later they were driving to a pound, Brooker at the wheel. Moody had a list of nine Sydney pounds and dogs' homes to visit.

'Why do you want photos?' Brooker asked. 'You haven't changed your mind about telling Idriess, have you?'

'No, he will never know if we can pull off a switch. But some day, maybe long after I'm gone, I want the *real* story told. Otherwise people will never forgive me for not doing everything to save Horrie, especially after what he did for us in war.'

'You've always been a real documenter!'

'We've had a lot worth recording, wouldn't you say?' Moody said, glancing at a map marking the pounds. The first visit was to one in Chatswood, north Sydney. They were shown around by an uninterested old man wearing a grubby green beanie and slippers that had seen better days. No dog resembling Horrie was in the line of filthy cages. Only mournful animals with searching, sad eyes watched as the two men peered in at them. Some growled; others cringed in corners; a few wagged tails in vain hope. They'd seen it all before: humans inspecting and then leaving without taking one of them; or the manager pushing another of their own into a cage.

'Most seem to look as if they are on death row,' Moody observed.

'They are,' the old man muttered without making eye contact.

'How long do they have?'

'On average six weeks, tops.'

'How are they . . . ?'

'Killed? Depends on which quarantine place bumps 'em off. Abbotsford does it the old fashioned way and shoots 'em between the eyes. The newer, fancier depots give 'em a cyanide pill in their food. They reckon it's more humane. I don't. A bullet is always quick and clean if you can shoot straight. Them pills can make it a much more agonising business, especially for the big, tough beasts. They can be in agony for an hour.' The old man then half-whispered, with a scintilla of compassion, 'Not right.'

Moody and Brooker drove on, looking for the second pound.

'He was a barrel of laughs, wasn't he?' Brooker said.

Moody examined the map before saying: 'Just like those poor condemned creatures.'

Brooker glanced at him. 'Bet you'd like to save 'em all, eh, Moods?'

Moody nodded: 'If I could afford it and give them all nice homes, yes.'

*

They saw three pounds on that Friday but the only dogs like Horrie were both Scottish terrier-crosses with long whiskers. One was black and male, the other white and female.

'They are about the same height,' Brooker noted, 'but it wouldn't work with them, even if you trimmed their whiskers.'

Moody lingered over the white dog. It wagged its tail and was friendly, without being demonstrative.

'I love this little girl,' he said. 'Just gorgeous!'

'C'mon, Moods. It's female. Forget it.'

'I know. I have something else in mind.'

'What?'

'Just something.'

That night Moody rang Idriess to tell him of the department's demands but without mentioning his attempt to find a Horrie substitute.

'You must write this bureaucrat Mr Wardle a letter,' Idriess said. 'Be contrite and polite. Accept responsibility. Tell him you saw a vet in Palestine and that Horrie was given a clean bill of health then admit you smuggled the dog home. Make sure he knows I have written a book about Horrie and that it will be published soon. Mention the Red Cross and how you offered the dog to them to raise funds. Point out that you could have kept the dog a secret but that helping this most worthy of causes seemed important enough to risk the consequences of exposure. Finish by appealing to him to spare Horrie, especially as he could still be used to raise funds for the Red Cross. That will put pressure on our Mr Wardle. Who knows? He may be a dog owner and a compassionate one at that!'

'I am not confident about his response,' Moody said, 'not the way his people have "attacked" so quickly with such vigour.'

'Oh,' Idriess said, ignoring him, 'also write a letter to the Prime Minister asking him to intervene.'

'Do you think there is any chance of that? Curtin's a busy man.'

'And a sick one. But even the fact that you write to him will be useful propaganda for the cause. You have to stir this up at the highest levels and keep the press interested.'

That evening Moody wrote a two-page letter to Wardle, and then another to Prime Minister Curtin. On Monday, 5 March, Moody and Brooker resumed their search for the replacement dog.

'There's a pound at Marrickville, the next suburb,' Moody said, 'but I think we should avoid it. It's the first place the authorities will check, if they suspect anything.'

They continued their search in south and west Sydney and ventured over the Harbour Bridge for another pound, but again without luck. After their search failed on Wednesday, they were becoming concerned. Moody had just one full day to find a dog before the Friday deadline.

'Marrickville is our last resort,' Moody told a despondent Brooker. 'We'll have to risk it.'

Early on Thursday, they set out for the pound, which was less than a kilometre from their Silver Street lodging. Moody asked the middle-aged, limping man in charge if he had any small dogs, 'like terriers.'

'We got one, guv'na,' the man said and Brooker engaged him by guessing correctly he was a cockney immigrant.

'Yeah, guv'na,' he replied with a big grin, 'fort on Gallipoli wiv you lot. Liked the Aussie style and decided to come art 'ere, didn't I?'

The stench of urine and dog hair was overwhelming in the heat. They reached a cage in a large shed which, unlike some of the other pounds, gave some shade in the hot early March weather. In it was a forlorn, small white dog. His face was furrier than Horrie's, but his body was not dissimilar, although it was not as long.

'What breed is he?' Moody asked.

'Dunno, guv,' the man chuckled, 'hardly ever come in 'ere well-dressed and wiv any papers, do dey?'

The others smiled. Without any discussion, they both knew this dog was the best option they had, and it was their last chance.

Moody and Brooker wandered to another cage, pretending to be interested in an old labrador.

'That little fella's not far off!' Brooker whispered.

'Body's not long enough. The snout's different. Not much, but different. But the ears are not nearly like Horrie's.'

'His coat is about right.'

'We have little choice,' Moody said, running his hand through his hair. 'Let's get a shot of it.'

'Got a name, has he?' Brooker said as they walked back to the manager. Moody handed Brooker his camera.

'Nar, guv. I just call 'em Bark One, Two, Three . . . Dis little bloke is Bark One. Been in 'ere since Christmas Day. Dey often come in den, don't they? People get careless at Christmas and just leave 'em in parks or streets or any-bloody-where. A bloody disgrace!'

Moody bent down and talked to the dog through the cage's wire. It approached. It bared its teeth and snarled. Brooker waited until the dog stopped its angry reaction and then took three photos.

'How old would you say he was?' Moody asked.

'Not too old, guv'na. You'll get a decade outa him, I'd say.'

'How much is he, mate?'

'For you, guv'na? Five bob.'

'That much?' Moody said, reaching for his wallet.

'You got a bob discount, dincha? See, Bark One can bite. Only occasionally mind. But he can be unfriendly, awright?'

'Yeah, yeah, I like him,' Moody said, keeping his apparent interest to a minimum. He handed the man five shillings. The man put on thick gardening gloves and opened the cage. The dog snapped at him and bit the glove. The man leashed the nervous little creature and said to it: 'Ain't you the lucky one, den?'

'Why is he lucky?' Moody asked.

'Bark One has been 'ere for more than two months. Only the holiday break in January has saved the little beggar from a firing squad. They would be coming for 'im and a couple of uvvers on Mondee or Tuesdee.'

Moody and Brooker drove the short distance to Silver Street with the despondent-looking dog on the back seat. It whimpered. The two men talked gently to it. Moody reached the back of his right hand towards it. The dog bit him on the forearm just above the wrist, drawing blood. A few minutes later at their lodging, Moody cleaned the bite and bandaged it. When he buttoned his shirt-sleeve and put on a coat, the bandage was hidden.

'What are we going to call the vicious little bugger?' Brooker asked.

'Horrie, of course!' Moody said.

'Sorry, stupid question! It's just that this one is so temperamentally different to Horrie.'

'With us, yes, but not anyone in Arab dress.'

'Good point.'

'Must have "Horrie" respond to his new name before I hand him over tomorrow.'

26

'HORRIE'S' EXECUTION

Moody took the substitute dog to a vet in Rosehill that afternoon. It did not appreciate its examination and managed to bite the gloved vet, Mr Kimber, on the hand and his young female assistant on the forearm.

'Should be put down for that,' short, rotund and bespectacled Kimber said as he dressed the wounds.

'I'm thinking about it.'

'No, seriously, Mr Moody; has he drawn human blood before?'

'Once that I know of.'

'Three bites give them a taste for it. It's like humans who murder. They often want more.' When Moody didn't respond, the vet added, 'It must be kept off the streets. I can put it down now, easily and quickly. I won't charge you.'

'No, I'll try to set it right.'

The vet gave an 'as you wish' shrug and asked Moody to hold the dog while he finished the examination. Moody was relieved to receive a perfect bill of health for the dog. He had this written out for the benefit of the authorities to verify that he had been responsible for a fit and well, rabies-free animal. Even in the short time they had together, the dog had responded a little to Moody's kindness and manner, especially when he was fed well.

'At least he has stopped biting the hand that feeds him,' Brooker observed.

'For the first, and maybe last time.'

'They're not going to put it down, are they? Not with that vet's report?'

'I just don't trust them.'

Moody had a sleepless night and got up on 9 March feeling depressed. He tried telling himself that this was the price that had to be paid for Horrie's survival. At breakfast, Brooker noticed Moody's melancholy.

'Don't tell me you've become attached to the little mutt already?' he asked, looking around at the dog.

Moody didn't respond.

'Look, Moods, you know it's for the greater good.'

'I know, I *know*.'

'Think of it this way, the fella at the pound said this animal was "for the firing squad" on Monday or Tuesday. The vet wanted to kill it off at the surgery. You've at least given it a couple of chances of a reprieve.'

'Won't help if Mr Wardle puts him down.'

'Has he replied to your letter?'

'No. That's what is making me nervous.'

It was another dry, sultry day and Moody was determined to take the dog in on his own. Brooker wanted to come with him for moral support.

'No,' Moody told him, 'they'll only become suspicious and you'd be implicated further.'

'But my picture was in the paper with him!' Brooker protested.

'That was a few weeks ago. Circumstances have changed.'

Moody, wearing a suit and tie, asked Brooker to take a photo of him walking to his car with the leashed dog, 'just for the record.'

'And maybe posterity,' Brooker said, securing the shot. Then he hailed a neighbour to take a shot of him and Moody with the dog.

'Why do you want to be in the shot?' Moody asked.

'Solidarity. The Rebels are with you all the way.'

Moody was touched. They shook hands.

*

When Brooker ushered a despondent Moody into the Rebels' surprise party for him on the night of Monday March 12, there was a real surprise: Horrie. The dog clawed at his thigh. Moody was overwhelmed. He held back tears as first Gill, then Fitzsimmons, Harlor, Shegog and Featherstone pressed forward to shake hands. Horrie had never been more energised. He bounced around the group, more pleased than any of them to be with his 'family' again.

With a beer in one hand, Moody shook his head and asked Brooker: 'Why isn't he at Cudgewa? I thought he was on his way, or at least there by now!'

'There was a delay in arranging a lift. I didn't want to worry you about it. Then I heard most of the boys would be in Sydney by now. So I asked that he be held back.'

'But . . . that's so dangerous!'

'Not now,' Gill said with a grin, 'Horrie is dead, remember? Brains blown out courtesy of our compassionate government.'

'Oh, shit,' Moody said, 'don't bloody remind me!'

Gill raised a glass and pointed to Horrie: 'To Horrie!' They all saluted him, and cried in chorus, 'the Mighty Aussie War Dog!!' Horrie loved the attention. He barked and trotted around the lounge room, much to the glee of the group.

'He's still in danger,' Moody half-protested.

'Don't worry, mate,' Gill said, putting an arm around his shoulder, 'I'll escort Horrie to Eddie Bennetts' farm myself.'

'I want to do it,' Moody said.

'You can't, mate, and you know it. The whole country has seen your photo in all the papers every day for weeks! If you are seen anywhere with Horrie, the game will be up. He'll really be dead meat.'

'And you, good Private Moody, Mr AWL, will be in jail,' Brooker added, tapping him on the chest.

'You're right,' Moody conceded, picking up Horrie and cuddling him. 'You and I won't be seeing each for a couple of months.'

In a ceremonial act, Horrie was presented with a massive bone, even bigger than the one he had been given in Palestine by the ever-grateful Barry the Butcher. To everyone's mirth, Horrie could hardly drag it. He saw the joke and was not offended. He just barked and wagged his tail. Then he settled down to gnaw on it where it was, his tail a constant reminder that he was enjoying himself on every imaginable level at this 'family' affair.

'You'll have to build a huge slit trench for this one, Horrie boy,' Fitzsimmons said, pretending to attempt to lift the bone as if it weighed a tonne.

The Rebels drank on, fuelled by stories of all their adventures. Someone asked about Murchison. Horrie pricked up those magnificent ears at the mention of his name. He circled the room, looking up at the Rebels.

'He remembers!' Shegog said. 'The little devil remembers!'

'Yeah well, Murchie made an impression on all of us,' Brooker said, and then, addressing the others, asked: 'Anyone heard anything about him?'

'Last I knew, he was in Java,' Harlor said. 'I've got a mate in 2/3 who said Murchie landed there with a forward contingent in February '42. A month later he was listed MIA.'

The room went quiet. Brooker poured himself another beer.

'I'll believe Murchie got knocked when someone tells me he witnessed it, not just the government saying he is *missing*,' he said. 'I'd want to know that his body was identified properly. Otherwise I'll never believe it. Murchie is a survivor. And he is just the type to disappear and start a new life somewhere.'

'Thousands of blokes are missing,' Fitzsimmons said.

'Thousands?' Gill said. 'You mean tens of thousands.'

Thoughts about Murchison's fate put the party in a sombre mood for a while. They drank on into the early hours of the next morning. Moody's sense of guilt about the execution of the substitute dog was temporarily salved, especially when they all agreed with Brooker's dictum: 'It was for the greater good, so that Horrie, who saved every one of us, could be an Aussie dog!'

Brooker pointed to Horrie, who sat wagging his tail. His ears were erect for a moment in a way chillingly yet wonderfully familiar to them all. 'To Horrie and a long, happy life as an Aussie dog! To Horrie!!'

The Rebels raised their glasses and responded in loud chorus: 'To Horrie!!'

27
HOAX OF THE CENTURY

Ion Idriess was sympathetic when Moody rang to tell him that 'Horrie' had been put down. But before the conversation was over, he was whipping Moody into action to take advantage of the incident. Everyone, every institution and the press had to be galvanised for a mass protest. Events began to unfold more or less as Idriess, the book's publisher and Moody planned. Moody, who had been at least an amateur actor of some accomplishment over his handling of Horrie, went along with the campaign of protest for 'the shameful putting down of an innocent war hero.'

Idriess wrote a poignant epitaph in his book, *Horrie the Wog Dog*, which was based loosely on Moody's reconstructed dairies and recollections:

Well, Horrie little fellow, your reward was death.
You who deserved a nation's plaudits, sleep in peace.
Among Australia's war heroes, we shall remember you.

The author was never to know that he too had been deceived in the interests of Horrie's survival.

The day after the substitute dog's extermination, the director from the Health Department, Wardle, became another victim of the Horrie hoax. He did not even bother to sign a reply to Moody. But he realised he had opened a Pandora's box of problems. He passed the issue higher and an indirect letter of response was written on Tuesday 13 March by J. H. L. Cumpston, the Director-General of Health, on behalf of the Commonwealth Minister for Health. They were further removed from the detail of the Horrie story, and on advice sided with Wardle's decision. Thus the deception over Horrie now reached into the highest political offices of the land, including that of the Prime Minister, John Curtin, whose huge in-box carried letters from Moody and scores of others concerning the dog. He replied to some, saying he could do nothing. Questions were asked in the House of Representatives concerning the 'Horrie tragedy' and members of parliament, responding to anger from their constituents, continued to pressure the government.

On 14 March, as directed and dictated by Idriess, Brooker wrote a letter to Sydney's *Daily Mirror* newspaper:

As the Sergeant of the Platoon of which 'Horrie' was a faithful cobber, I would like to express my sentiments regarding the callous way in which he was done to death. I can scarcely believe that such inhumanity exists in the world, least of all in a country where we boast of our glorious Freedom, (?) and sense of fair play. Realising that space is limited, I am unable to write as my indignation and horror urge me to do, but I hope from the bottom of my heart that those who directed this wanton destruction of a famous and lovable animal spend the remainder of their days as sleeplessly as has been my lot since the passing of my well loved pal.
Faithfully yours
R Brooker.

The press then went into overdrive in milking the 'tragic tale' of Horrie's execution, supported, as Wardle predicted, by the World League for the Protection of Animals, the RSL and many other interested parties. Moody and Brooker organised 6th Division to carry out a funeral for the dog, although there was no body in the coffin. Quarantine had refused to hand it over, saying it had to be incinerated. The press covered the funeral.

Moody gambled on releasing the photo to the press of him walking with the substitute dog on the morning he took it to the Quarantine Station. Gill and Brooker worried that someone would pick the differences in the two dogs.

'No, it'll be okay,' Moody assured them, 'the dog is only a small part of the shot. You'd have to know what to look for. Besides, we've created an illusion. Everyone believes Horrie was executed.'

Moody had the difficult task of writing to his father, telling him of 'Horrie's' demise. He made several attempts, and it gave him more than an inkling of the depth of the deception he was creating. His final draft was crisp and brief. Henry was distressed when he received it. He collected himself and replied:

> I know by my own feelings just how you feel over this business, but remember Jim that time heals most things and do not do anything rash in the meantime . . . I have been inundated with telephone calls, some of them trunk line calls from servicemen both AIF and RAAF, and many from chaps I have never heard of before, and also newspaper reporters. The outrage [over the dog's killing] with all its contemptible treachery and cunning has caused some considerable stir here . . . Whatever happens [with protests] Jim, I want you to keep away from any active part in it. You have nothing to blame yourself for. You did a splendid job for the little dog while he was alive . . . No doubt you will be a marked man for some time and if any lawlessness occurred you would probably be framed for it.

Henry had remained in control in the letter but despite his advice to his son, could not resist writing a protest letter himself to the Melbourne's *Sun* that concluded: 'It seemed a senseless, malicious act to kill a harmless animal which brought so much joy to our boys.'

Moody was depressed reading his father's reply to him and the letter to the paper. He felt more guilt for deceiving his father than anyone else but did not have time to dwell on it, such was the ongoing attention on the story. Articles and features continued to appear and the focus of the nation was on the story. It was a tabloid dream for most editors. Sydney's *Daily Mirror* ran it from every possible angle, including, for the sake of balance, the view of Wardle and his department. Wardle fell into the trap of defending his position by saying that he was making an example of the animal and its illegal entry, even when it was admitted that the dog in question was in perfect condition. This ran contrary to the much-vaunted Australian philosophy of a 'fair go.'

Wardle also tried to justify his decision in letters to key government and military officials. Typical was one written to Lieutenant-Colonel K. S. McIntosh in which he noted that:

> During March and April [1942] there were 19 vessels carrying troops and on which were animal mascots, mainly dogs. 21 dogs, 17 monkeys, 1 cat, 1 rabbit, 1 pigeon, 1 duck, 3 squirrels and 1 mongoose were destroyed; so it is quite possible that a small number of animals were surreptitiously landed . . . Since July 1942, when the worst of the troop movements were over, many animals were destroyed or died on overseas ships at Australian ports; some were seized, others destroyed at the request of Masters, who were not prepared to

> enter into bonds for the security of the animals. They included: 5 cattle; 45 sheep; 14 pigs; 9 goats; 185 dogs; 136 cats; 142 birds and 18 miscellaneous animals.

Just to show that he was a proud bureaucrat doing his diligent duty, he concluded the letter with: 'You will see from this that our Quarantine Officers are on the job.'

Wardle continued, perhaps deliberately, to misconstrue Horrie being called a 'Wog Dog,' as if this implied he had disease and not the fact that it was an Australian colloquial expression for Middle Easteners.

Wardle would have escaped vilification if Horrie had not had such a remarkable war record in army service. For the sake of bureaucratic intransigence, he misjudged public reaction. His stubborn adherence to understandable, necessary 'regulations' overruled a rational, fair and appropriate response to an individual case of overwhelming merit. Had Wardle served in war, or done a minimum of homework on the case, he would have been aware of Horrie's importance to the thousand fighting men of the 2/1 Machine Gun Battalion. He had gone after Horrie and Moody with a fervour only outweighed by the opprobrium heaped upon him for his decision. Wardle released a statement that said: 'It is directed that the Deputy-Crown Solicitor should be consulted with reference to launching a prosecution against the person who illegally imported the dog. Approval has been obtained to prosecute.'

But public pressure was so strong that no moves were made against Moody or any of the Rebels. Yet attacks on Wardle stepped up in outbursts in letters to him and the press, some which threatened physical violence. One typical message, unsigned but for a serviceman's serial number—NX31236—said: 'a few of us would like to see the photo of the one responsible for this masterpiece of red tape [over the dog's killing].'

A Mr A. C. Bendrodt, from a prominent Sydney family, went public. His photo was carried in reports in which he said that Wardle was 'guilty of unnecessary brutality' over the extermination.

Another person, calling himself 'Y. S., an old soldier' of Chatswood, Sydney, ended his letter with: 'I hope and pray that when your day comes I will have the pleasure to put you to sleep in the same way as that little mate [Horrie] died.'

More worrying was a further unsigned message, which said: 'I was trained to kill in the Great War and I am still a very accurate shot. Your [Wardle's] killing of this creature of God deserves a similar fate and I know how to do it.'

Another, signing him or herself 'Dog Lovers of the World', wrote:

> Dog Murderer,
>
> Please do us a big favour & on your way home today buy yourself a dose of arsenic or something that makes a slow deaf [sic].

The many threats did not fall on deaf ears. Wardle was more than concerned. He wanted to sue the letter writers and journalists commenting on the case for libel. He wrote to the federal government's Crown Solicitor asking if legal action could be taken. The Crown replied that 'it could not be established that any real injury was done to the reputation' of Wardle, and that any 'verdict obtained [for Wardle]' would only gain 'nominal damages.' In other words, it was not worth going to court over.

Wardle was not alone in feeling the heat. The unfortunate New South Wales Minister for Health, C. A. Kelly, came under scrutiny and was labelled 'one of the most unpopular men in Sydney' for his alleged putting to death of Horrie. Kelly denied that he had anything to do with the case, which was a federal, not a state matter, and he feared he would lose his seat at the next election. He was vilified, he claimed, by strangers and even a small boy, who 'complained to a member of my staff about the cruelty I am supposed to have done.'

The *Truth* newspaper, which loved scandal, dwelt on the story with features such as 'Legal Murder of War Dog Executed by Red Tape.' Articles were often accompanied by Moody's photographs from the war and afterwards, which verified and authenticated the heroic tale with its shock ending. Moody again took a gamble by releasing the photograph of him, Brooker and the dog on the morning of 9 March when he took the fake Horrie to the Quarantine Station. But the medium front-on shot of the dog, dwarfed in the photo, would need expert scrutiny to distinguish it from the real Horrie, especially if the latter had his ears pinned back and was not on alert.

Moody had a phone call from Barry Bain, the butcher, who was now working in Sydney. He was angry and upset about Horrie. He ranted on the phone, attacking even Moody for not doing enough to save Horrie. Moody was forced to interrupt: 'Barry, Barry, Barry,' he said, 'listen! What did I tell you when we were based near Tel Aviv, and you thought we were going to leave him with the Ascalon Police?'

'What?'

'What did I tell you?'

'That I shouldn't worry, you had a plan for him.'

'Well, I am saying it again.'

There was silence on the line before Barry understood what he was being told.

'Oh . . . you mean . . . ?'

'Yes . . . but please, mate, keep it under your hat. All right?'

The Rebels had a meeting at a pub in Sydney's Woollahra on 20 March and Moody asked the others if they should find a partner for Horrie.

'He'll need a companion like Imshi,' he said. After several rounds of beer, they passed around the hat and collected £3, which would be used to purchase a suitable female for Horrie, who would be sent to Cudgewa.

'Where are you going to find it?' Featherstone asked.

'I've already met *her*,' Moody said with a wry smile, 'and I'm going to show her to the world.'

The next day Moody returned to the pound he had visited a few weeks earlier when looking for the Horrie substitute and bought the cute little white Scottish terrier for seven shillings. He then alerted the press and fuelled his grand deception by telling reporters he had bought a dog to replace Horrie. Subsequent articles had photos of Moody with the 'new' dog.

A reporter from the *Mirror* asked him if she had a name.

'Imshi II,' he said poker-faced.

'Imshi? What's that mean?'

Moody gave a brief description of the original Imshi, 'Horrie's companion in Palestine and Syria.'

The press lapped it up. The caption for the photo in the *Truth* of 25 March read: 'Jim Moody, saddened by the loss of Horrie, now has a new canine pal, a Scotty, one Imshi II. But Jim will never stop mourning the loss of his Wog cobber, Horrie.'

Whenever the story settled down, Moody planned to take Imshi II to Cudgewa to mate her with Horrie.

*

The ongoing 'tragic' story of Horrie's 'death' created a huge public response right across the nation. Papers were flooded with letters and commentary into April. Moody became an overnight martyr-hero, himself receiving hundreds of letters of sympathy and support, with scores of people offering help, some with funds, to take his protest further. Ninety-nine per cent of the letters to the press condemned the authorities for their callous disregard and lack of flexibility and humanity. Many were so touched that they burst into verse with poignant poems. Typical was one written by Laura Eveline Dixon that began:

A hero passed, when stilled the splendid heart
Of that brave dog who played in War his Part.
A waif from out the desert, he attained
By right a page in history, and surely gained
The love of everyone who knows the worth
Of canine comradeship upon this earth.

It was heartfelt. Doggerel predominated. A person signing himself 'Charlie' wrote:

Now Horrie's gone far far away,
He'll no more see the light of day,
His life is done, they blew him up,
And never more we'll see our pup.

The passionate response reached a crescendo a week before Anzac Day 1945 when a public protest meeting was held in the basement of the Sydney Town Hall. Moody and Idriess spoke at the meeting. Wardle was singled out for suggested 'punishment;' a demand was made for the Commonwealth government to amend regulations; and the Prime Minister was petitioned to prevent anything 'similar happening to gallant pets of servicemen returning to this country.'

On Anzac Day itself, wreaths were solemnly laid for Horrie (and would be for another 20 years) at the Cenotaph in Martin Place, Sydney. Prominent among them was one from the 6th Division, inscribed: 'In Memory of our pal, Horrie, the Wog Dog.'

The tabloids showed a picture of Private J. M. Creer, 'WX40960,' saluting the wreaths placed for Horrie on the Cenotaph.

The papers also reported that 'a small boy' called at Sydney's Red Cross House and asked what he could do with a wreath he had made. It was adorned with a Union Jack he had drawn himself, and a message: 'In memory of Horrie, the Digger's Friend of the Middle East—From Mickie Wilson.'

Moody kept it running by letting the press know he had written to the boy, enclosing a photo of Horrie. By taking up every press opportunity, Moody was maintaining his public rage for the benefit of the government and the bureaucracy. After the story died down, he would have to tread carefully, he reasoned, for the rest of his life, to maintain the fiction about Horrie's demise. This was especially with so many influential people and institutions duped. Moody also felt the responsibility to the Rebels, who were all implicated in the supreme cover-up and hoax, the most successful in Australian history.

Barry the Butcher, the only character outside the Rebels who had an idea of the 'fraud,' found the group in a private room at the Woollahra pub late in the afternoon on Anzac Day. They had been drinking since the march in Sydney's streets finished at noon. He wanted to know the full story, but they refused to tell him. Yet Moody reassured him that his 'little mate' was safe and well.

'One day,' Moody assured him, 'I'll let you see for yourself.'

That was enough for Barry, who was allowed to join them for the rest of a most convivial evening.

*

The Horrie story had become a national issue that had a life of its own. An official memorial was proposed by the Royal Society for the Prevention of Cruelty to Animals. Readers of its magazine, *Animals,* were asked to provide funds, but Moody never endorsed this development, believing it would be a monument to his own grand deception, no matter how it was justified to him by Brooker and the Rebels as 'for the greater good.' The monument was never built. (In 1955, a decade later, the RSPCA was accused of doing nothing with the £81 raised for the Horrie memorial.) But Moody was happy to be linked to a Sydney *Daily Telegraph* appeal for funds to invoke the memory of Horrie in order to keep open the King Edward's Dogs Home in Moore Park, Sydney. That appeased Moody's soul a fraction, with the substitute dog forever on his conscience. By helping to keep the home operating, he was doing his bit to ensure that hundreds of other dogs survived.

The continued public clamour over 'Horrie' had a direct impact on a further illegal animal import case. In April, another dog, called 'Dinah,' who belonged to a former officer of the 2nd AIF, was condemned to death for similar allegations to those thrown at Horrie. But this time Wardle relented and spared Dinah. This again helped Moody justify to himself the merit of his actions over Horrie and the substitute dog. Reacting to Wardle's backdown this time, Moody said: 'It's a case of once bitten, twice shy.'

The dignified office of the Prime Minister deemed it appropriate to keep replying to 'sensible and rational' letters concerning the Horrie story but they were not from John Curtin. He died on 5 July 1945 and was replaced by Ben Chifley, who had the unenviable task of sifting through the massive correspondence that had piled up in the office during Curtin's debilitating last months. The letters from Chifley's private secretary, E. W. Tonkin, concerning Horrie began to flow in September. One example was a reply to a 21 September letter to the Prime Minister written by a Mrs Mateer, of Lithgow, New South Wales, who had wanted him to act on the 'barbarous act perpetrated on Horrie.' The response, dictated by Chifley to his secretary, said:

> I have been requested by the Prime Minister to acknowledge the receipt of your letter relative to "Horrie the Wog Dog". Mr Chifley wishes me to say that he is unable to help you in the direction desired.

This reply demonstrated that the sting had gone out of the Horrie incident after half a year of intense coverage and scrutiny. While the story had attracted a big following it was not quite one of the issues then galvanising the nation in August and September, such as the end of the Pacific War and Japan's unconditional surrender after the two atomic weapons had been dropped on Hiroshima on 6 August, and Nagasaki on 9 August 1945.

Moody was pleased and most relieved with the subsidence of the Horrie 'issue.' His brazen scheme had worked far beyond his wildest expectations. Now it was apparently over, he hoped that he and Horrie could carry on their lives under far less strain or scrutiny. But the scam had touched Moody more than anyone else. He felt an ongoing sense of guilt for deceiving so many people from the Prime Minister down, and including his father, the Machine Gun battalion, the entire 6th Division, the media and the public. Moody would love to have told the world that Horrie was alive and safe, but instead he had to maintain the subterfuge over a tale that would never leave him. Every day of his life he was reminded by somebody or an incident, of the story.

The only people he shared the ruse with were the Rebels and Barry the Butcher, with a very few exceptions over the decades. One was a young journalist, Norma James, whom he met in the seaside town of Wollongong, 82 kilometres south of Sydney. Moody, still a celebrity, was on a photographic assignment in February 1946, 11 months after the execution of the substitute dog. They talked about Horrie. James told journalist Anthony Hill that Moody said to her: 'I'll tell you something one day.' Moody took her notebook and pencil and wrote: 'Horrie is not dead. He never died. But if you tell anyone I'll deny it.'

Soon afterwards, he revealed the tale in more detail to James.

'You don't think an Australian soldier would leave a mate like that, do you?' he said to her.

Years later Betty Featherstone, the wife of Brian, recalled a 'half-drunk' Moody talking and laughing about the hoax. At every Anzac Day reunion he would drink heavily with those wartime mates and relive the story in every amusing and dramatic detail. Moody found those days cathartic. For a few precious hours annually he did not have to live a lie. He and the Rebels could wallow in private over their coup.

"I was supposed to be the joker in our pack,' Bert Fitzsimmons said to Moody more than once at these special reunions, 'but you have pulled off the prank of the century!'

28
POSTSCRIPT

Horrie lived in idyllic surroundings on a dairy farm at Cudgewa owned by Eddie Albert Bennetts, a friend of Moody's from the 6th Division who had fought with the Tank-Attack (formerly Anti-Tank) Battalion. Horrie sired two litters of seven pups with his partner, Ishmi II. Over the years, most of the Rebels managed to visit Horrie at least once and Barry the Butcher was known to have made the trip from Sydney six times.

Moody kept in contact with Horrie and on average made monthly visits to him, keeping Imshi II and the pups with his (Moody's) family. He decided with Bennetts to give Horrie the new name of 'Benji'—an amalgam of *Ben*netts and *Ji*m. Calling him Horrie would have been dangerous. Word would have leaked out that a dog fitting the famous animal's description was alive and well. Moody was based in several places within a few hours drive of Cudgewa.

It gave him great joy to see his beloved mate happy and contented into his maturity. Horrie always greeted him (and Imshi II) with unbridled enthusiasm, as if thanking him for his wonderful life that his master's many risky actions had given him. Horrie was closer to Eddie Bennetts' wife Gladys because Eddie was not comfortable with dogs around cattle.

On one occasion at a Melbourne reunion on Anzac Day in the late 1940s, Moody, Bennetts and several of the Rebels got themselves merry. As usual Moody was ready for some spirited behaviour. He took Bennetts, Featherstone and Gill for a hair-raising ride in the old Rolls Royce he had converted into a moveable workshop for his wool-classing operations. Imshi II was in the car. Moody, in a reckless mood, careered through Melbourne's beautiful Treasury Gardens, where vehicles never travelled. The thrill-ride ended up with them all partying at a nearby pub. Eddie Bennetts noticed Moody left the celebrations several times in the night. The next morning his intermittent departures were explained. He had been with Imshi in the Rolls, helping to deliver four pups sired by Horrie.

At age ten years, Horrie was overweight and slowed up by severe bouts of rheumatism in his back. This less-than-nimble condition led to him being accidentally run over and killed at Log Bridge near Cudgewa. Moody was devastated by the news. But all the Rebels consoled him by reminding him that had he not taken Horrie out of the Libyan Desert he would have died there as a pup. Hundreds of men of the 2/1 Machine Gun Battalion and many more in units of 6th Division then would have been killed and injured by German Stukas in Greece, Crete and Palestine, on the high seas and on land.

'Every dog has his day,' Moody said, 'and except for a week or so in Syria, Horrie was on top of life, *every* day.'

Horrie's sad demise drew Moody closer to Imshi and the pups, and he often commented to his family about 'all the little Horries running around.'

Imshi died in 1959, aged 14. Moody gained great personal satisfaction from knowing that Horrie's fine genes lived on through many offspring, and that he and the Rebels had beaten the system. But the long-running sting did not end there. In 1966, 21 years after the ruse by Moody and the Rebels, he felt comfortable enough to donate Horrie's 'uniform' and his mode of travel, the pack, to the Australian War Memorial in Canberra. Included were an Africa Star, ribbon, colour patch, and chevrons: his insignias indicating rank and length of service. These were displayed by the Memorial and the event created another round of publicity on the story. But Moody kept the EX1 tag and RSL medallion as keepsakes for his own vivid memories. They were his equivalent to the sock given to Horrie to always remember Moody by. Being a professional photographer he also kept stylish snaps of Horrie, Imshi II and their pups.

*

Jim Moody gained fame from his association with Horrie but his life was never the same after his traumatic war and the dramatic events of 1945. The government noted his record of being AWL, and also his attacks on its Health Department, and decided he was not eligible for any soldier settlement block. He ran his Manly photography shop for a while and also worked for another photographic business, Peter Fox Studios in Melbourne. He and Don Gill enjoyed a couple of years after the war as daredevil motorbike racers at Sydney and Melbourne speedways. He and Gill were always able to provide spectacular acts, which had been practised and honed in Libya's Western Desert in 1941.

Moody kept in contact with all the Rebels and they would have a reunion every Anzac Day for two decades after the war. Most of the group would make it to Melbourne and take a private room at the Bowling Club in Union Street in the suburb of Windsor. As the decades rolled on, the dispersed group members were down to phone calls, cards and letters. Moody had divorced during the war after his wife became involved with another man in Melbourne. In 1948, he met Joan Booth, an army nursing lieutenant, and they married in 1951 (the same year Brian Featherstone married his wife Betty). When asked what attracted her to Moody, Joan replied after some thought: 'His sense of humour.'

Betty Featherstone agreed with that Moody characteristic and added that he was 'a larrikin with a good heart.'

The lack of a base caused Moody to be peripatetic in his search for work. Each of their three children, Leonie,

Ian and Ann, was born in a different part of Victoria. Moody was never able to settle down and he developed a drinking problem brought on by his war and the pressures and consequences of defending Horrie's life. He also had intermittent nightmares, over his war experiences, including Stuka attacks, the deaths of the girls of the Larissa convent, Horrie and the substitute dog. They never abated. He and Joan divorced in 1957.

Moody married a third time but again he was unsettled, although he held down a good job for more than 20 years as a wool-classer for Southern Farmers, working the many shearing sheds in western Victoria's Portland and Hamilton districts. His third marriage ended in the late 1960s. In the mid-1970s he became involved with an Adelaide woman, Natalie Thompson. She was a hotelier, which suited Moody's lifestyle.

There was one further dog 'incident.' He was doing some classing at a big grazier's property in Victoria when a farmer objected forcefully to his then dog, a kelpie, being on his property. It brought back memories of incidents involving Horrie in 1941 at Ikingi with the sergeant-of-the guard, and also with the Nazi spy in the Greek village. Moody got into an altercation with the farmer. This was reported to Moody's employer, but such was his standing as a wool-classer and admired character that his employer supported him in preference to keeping the major client. In the end the client allowed Moody back on his property with the kelpie to do further wool-classing.

Another event demonstrated the extent of his

drinking, when he was picked up by Portland Police after his involvement in a car accident in 1975 at age 64. He was given a blood test. Even though he bad-mouthed the arresting policemen, they did not charge him. This was in part because of his local popularity. When Moody asked for the result of his blood alcohol level, the doctor on duty told him: 'It's okay, you're fine; there was no blood in the sample.'

Brian Featherstone's situation as the senior cop in Colac, Victoria, was just another reason that Moody would never disclose the true Horrie story publicly. All the Rebels could have been charged with perjury and several other offences for the complicity in the Horrie smuggling and subsequent cover-up. It would have ended Featherstone's career in the police force. None of the Rebels would have been given land after the war. As it was, their reputations had led to some of them not receiving good blocks in commercial or valued locations.

Moody lived out his days with Natalie at Portland in an old tram car in the bush, and in the depth of winter in Adelaide. In typically cynical, yet fatalistic fashion, he called the tram car The Last Stop. A Rebel to the end, he ran the tram car's electricity system on kerosene, but had trouble with local authorities for short-circuiting and blacking out the Portland region when using a double adaptor. It led to his tram car being properly wired.

Moody died in 1979, aged 68. His son Ian carried out one of his father's last wishes that the tram car should 'not end up on the scrap heap.' Ian arranged for it to be donated to Portland's Vintage Car Club where it is on permanent display.

Jim Moody's efforts on behalf of a lost and doomed dog in a Libyan desert form an integral, if unusual part of the enduring Anzac legend of mateship and high sacrifice. No one who knew Horrie ever doubted that every risk and effort for this exceptional animal was merited. Moody's love of dogs caused him much personal loss, but he was first to say, without equivocation, it was all worth it for Horrie, *the grand dog of war*.

ACKNOWLEDGEMENTS

Research for the book was undertaken in Australia, the UK, Libya, Egypt, Israel (Palestine), Greece, Crete, Syria and New Guinea. The main sources were varied and included the National Archives of Australia; the Australian War Memorial; the 2/1st Machine Gun Battalion Unit History; the 2/3 Machine Gun Battalion Unit History; 2/1 Anti-Tank History; 2/18th Brigade official history; 6th Division official history. A special thanks to the Tel Aviv based Mike Guy, a former Israeli paratrooper, for his expert guidance through his country and for his contacts throughout the Middle East. Again (as with my previous books on the Middle East: *The Australian Light Horse* and *Bill the Bastard*), advice from Susan Scollay on Syria and Lebanon was important for my research there.

Thanks also to those who granted interviews or who let me view data, photos, unpublished diaries, letters and files and other information. They included Major-General James Barry, Ed Bennetts (the son of Eddie and Gladys Bennetts), Ian Bartholemew, Gill Bozer, Betty Featherstone, Jack Grossman, Jane Hickey, Anthony Hill, Thos Hodgson, Carl Johnson, Richard Joslin, Leon Levin, George Manousakis, Tony Maylam, Ian Moody (son of Jim), Joan Moody (second wife of Jim), Leonie Moody (daughter of Jim), Aladin Rahemtula, Andrew Rule, former Ambassador to Syria, Tammam Sulaiman, Greg Thomas, Lyn Thomas, and Sarah Wells.

A special acknowledgement to publisher Sue Hines for her support over five books at publisher Allen & Unwin: *Program for Puppet, Blood is a Stranger, Faces in the Rain, Bill the Bastard* and *Horrie the War Dog.*

This book includes dramatisations and re-creations based on information from the above sources.